TWO MOUNTAINS
AND A RIVER

H. W. TILMAN

Looking west from camp on south-west spur of Rakaposhi

TWO MOUNTAINS AND A RIVER

H. W. TILMAN

TILMAN

First published 1949 by Cambridge University Press
This edition published 2016 by Tilman Books
www.tilmanbooks.com
a joint venture by
Lodestar Books www.lodestarbooks.com
and Vertebrate Publishing www.v-publishing.co.uk

Cover design by Jane Beagley
Vertebrate Graphics Ltd. www.v-graphics.co.uk

Lodestar Books has asserted their right
to be identified as the Editor of this Work

Series editor Dick Wynne
Series researcher Bob Comlay

A CIP catalogue record for this book
is available from the British Library

ISBN 978-1-909461-30-7

Typeset in Baskerville from Storm Type Foundry
Printed and bound by Pulsio, Bulgaria
All papers used by Tilman Books are sourced responsibly

MIX
Paper from
responsible sources
FSC® C128169
FSC
www.fsc.org

Contents

Photographs

Maps

Foreword

Gerda Pauler

M Y LOVE FOR THE HIMALAYA AND CENTRAL ASIA goes back to the 1980s, and more than twenty journeys have led me to these regions up to now. Whenever there had been time left at the end of a trip I used to bide my time in local bookshops looking for travel accounts; preferably old ones. On one of these occasions I bought *When Men and Mountains Meet* (1946) yet though I enjoyed reading the book it never struck me to look for others written by Harold William 'Bill' Tilman. Today, I have to admit that this omission was a big mistake, and if I was asked to describe *Two Mountains and a River* with one word only I would say: outstanding.

However, what makes a travel account an outstanding one? It was not before the age of thirty that Tilman's career as a mountaineer and explorer started. Together with his friend Eric Shipton they soon became the 'great climbing duo of the interwar years' and they attempted or climbed several mountains in Africa before moving the focus to the Himalaya. Although Tilman either led or took part in remarkable expeditions (first ascent Nanda Devi, and leading a Mount Everest Expedition where he and three others reach 8320m) *Two Mountains and a River* is virtually free of pointing out any of these achievements. This lack of flaunting himself makes Tilman the most likable person, who allows the reader to join him as an equal partner on an extraordinary journey. Whereas many climbing writers (or writing climbers) revel in self-centred, lengthy descriptions of ascents or explorations, Tilman, who probably led one of the most adventurous lives of the twentieth century, shows humbleness and understanding for people around him; even for those who make life difficult or miserable for him. Tilman—the silent man.

9

Language fascinates me, and more than once I stopped reading a book because I deemed an author's vocabulary or wording dull, repetitive or inadequate. Tilman's vocabulary is wide yet his language is far from being flowery, pompous or overdone. For every single detail or situation he describes he employs the right expression or tone. As a result, Tilman does not get lost in lengthy portrayals of events but takes the reader along his way at the most pleasant pace. Additionally, he shows a high level of knowledge regarding quotes that supplement his narration perfectly without seeking to attract attention by puffiness.

The most striking characteristic however, is Tilman's sense of humour in even the most demanding and challenging situations. Yet, set against the backdrop of the hardship he had to endure in both World Wars, it clearly needs more than a heavy backpack, a rifle-waving local warlord or a seemingly endless climb to throw a man like Tilman off balance. I had a couple of hearty laughs and smiled my way through 250 pages.

To use Bob Comlay's words: 'He (Tilman) left a legacy of some of the finest travel books ever written.' *Two Mountains and a River* is one of them.

Preface

IN THE OPINION OF DR JOHNSON "the adventurer upon unknown coasts and the describer of distant lands is always welcomed as a man who has laboured for others". To one who generally has travelled to please only himself this is a reassuring thought, and in the hope that it is true I have here described some distant lands visited in 1947.

The reader will notice a remarkable difference between Robert Kappeler's photographs (the majority of the first twenty-three plates) and those of the author, and had he been with us to watch the painstaking, methodical eagerness of the one, and the slap-dash, snap-happy carelessness of the other he would not be surprised. Nevertheless, lack of skill and care is not the sole reason for the poor results, for there was a defect in my camera. But the discovery of this, like most of the important discoveries of one's life, was made too late.

I am once more indebted to Dr R.J. Perring for much criticism and help, and to R.T. Sneyd, Esq. for revising the proofs; also to J.M.K. Vyvyan, Esq. for the Pl. 15 photograph.

H.W.T.
Barmouth
1948

Map 1: The Whole Story

CHAPTER I

FOOD AND EQUIPMENT

—◆—

THE WORST PART OF A WAR, as many of us are beginning to realise, is the end. For the majority war can be at worst an inconvenience and may even be advantageous; but just as vice and indulgence often result in disease and poverty, war has after-effects no less dreadful. And we are the less prepared to withstand the shock of these effects because while war is in progress our political prophets, amateur and professional, feel it their duty to keep up our spirits with words of present hope and, more particularly, future comfort—pie in the sky, in fact. In the late war, though careless talk, as it was called, about military matters was almost indictable, anyone was free to indulge in careless talk about the new and better world which would emerge refined, as they put it, from the crucible of war. And both those old enough to know better and those young enough to think more cheerfully availed themselves of this licence.

For many, therefore, life became even more earnest, almost a crusade; they returned from the war resolved to better not only themselves but their unfortunate fellows. Not all, however, were taken in by this talk of a new heaven and a new earth. Some had heard it before during an earlier and better war and were therefore sceptical, while others although not content were prepared to put up with the old. These, the minority, feeling that standing still was better than progress in the wrong direction, and mindful of the words of Ecclesiasticus, 'be not over busy in thy superfluous works', and who were too old, perhaps, to change or too stupid to see the need of change—these, instead of looking about for a new reel, made what pathetic haste they could to pick up the broken threads of their pre-war lives. Among these modern Bourbons, so to speak, I counted myself, and my survey of the war-shattered world in the autumn of 1945 was directed naturally to the Himalaya, to the ways and means of getting there, and to the chances of finding like-minded survivors with the same extravagant ideas. So loud and all-prevalent was the din raised by the planners of the new world that it was hardly possible for me to avoid absorbing something of the spirit of the times, so that I did feel some slight uneasiness at attempting to do once more what I wanted to do as opposed to what the mandarins might expect me to do. But I argued as Falstaff did about stealing, it was my vocation, 'and 'tis no sin for a man to labour in his vocation'.

Just as after the first war, when one took stock, shame mingled with satisfaction at finding oneself still alive. One felt a bit like the Ancient Mariner; so many better men, a few of them friends, were dead:

> And a thousand thousand slimy things
> Lived on; and so did I.

But casualties were not solely responsible for the absence of like-minded companions. Though interest in mountaineering and explora-tion was, or seemed to be, greater than ever, I could find no one who was either brazen enough to turn his back on the promised land or who was not indispensable to a planned economy. Still, if one is bent on travel or exploration rather than on mountaineering, provided one has the strength of will or the prudence to resist the challenge of the higher peaks, it is practicable to wander in the Himalaya without other companions than Sherpas. In 1946 I would gladly have done this but there were more serious hindrances to be overcome.

In 1946 England could be compared to the married state—those who were out (most of the Services) wishing frantically to get in, while many who were in wished as much to get out and found it devilish hard. For a few months in the beginning of 1946 I fluttered about like a bird in a cage beating my head vainly against the bars of shipping offices which had no ships, stores which had no equipment, and export and currency regulations which would not yield. My reward in the end was but one short flutter to Switzerland, official negligence or short-sighted planning having temporarily left that door of the cage open.

Early in 1947, as would-be travellers will remember, there was a kind of false dawn before darkness descended again; the bonds were slightly eased while fresh knots were being tied, and the Continental traveller having been given enough rope duly hanged himself. Travel at home and abroad became easier that spring and summer, and Mr

Bevin's generous vision of a world of visa-less travel had in one or two countries been realised. Shipping firms when asked for a passage no longer laughed sardonically, but deigned to accept £10 in return for a single comfortless passage to Bombay under more or less military discipline in a 'dry' trooper; equipment of a kind could be ordered and even obtained if several months' grace was given; if it was to be taken abroad no coupons were needed, while pemmican, as I belatedly discovered, was not rationed. By 1947 great numbers of VIPs, the chief obstacle to private travel, had been redistributed or recalled, either to gratify some distant fragment of the dumb herd with their presence or to leave it to bemoan their loss, so that at length the ordinary man by cunning, luck, or impudence, stood some chance of having his wants attended to.

By 1947 my modest arrangements for a journey to one of the less well-known parts of the Karakoram were all but complete—passage booked, equipment ordered, and three Sherpa porters engaged. The Survey of India had promised to arrange for a surveyor to accompany me, for in this utilitarian age it is more than ever necessary to have some scientific or quasi-scientific purpose—to assume a virtue though you have it not. If one wants to go to the North Pole to collect cosmic dust, to the bottom of the sea for globigerina ooze, or to Patagonia to count the number of albinos, money and every facility are readily available. But an aimless wanderer is not pleasing to the mandarins. The only hitch in my arrangements was that permission to go through Kashmir had not yet been received from the authorities at Srinagar.

The porters had been engaged through our old friend and companion of many expeditions, Angtharkay, who had now blossomed out as a transport agent in Darjeeling, fertilised no doubt by the numbers of Americans and British who had visited Darjeeling and Sikkim during the war. Through him ponies, porters, cooks, and anything else needful could be obtained, but unluckily neither he himself nor any porter that I knew was available this year. Many were engaged, some were absent, and, according to Angtharkay's report, drink and the devil had done for the rest; for the Sherpa is not a perfect specimen of economic man—what he gets he spends, usually on drink or gambling. To this rule Angtharkay is an exception, but then as his record shows he has many other qualities not usually found in Sherpas. This

year he and twenty other Sherpas were going to Sikkim and eastern
Nepal with a large party, the members of which had not to disguise
themselves as scientists for they were the thing itself. The flora, fauna,
entomology, morphology, and geology of Sikkim having been exhaus-
tively examined, there was left only the snow, and this they were going
to measure.

In February while waiting impatiently for the expected permission
from the Kashmir Durbar, I received an invitation to join two experienced Swiss mountaineers, Hans Gyr and Robert Kappeler, who were
going to the Himalaya under the aegis of the 'Schweizerische Stiftung
für ausseralpine Forschungen' or 'Swiss Foundation for Mountain
Exploration'. This Foundation is a private affair—quite independent
of the government—whose purpose is to encourage, organise, and
assist the dispatch of mountaineering expeditions to any part of the
world. It has financed one expedition in the past, and is in a position
to finance others, but naturally prefers that such expeditions should
be financially independent. It is primarily concerned with mountaineering rather than scientific exploration. An expedition under the
patronage of the Foundation is expected to concede the copyright of
all photographs, articles, or books which are the result of the expedition's work to the Foundation. Naturally this arrangement would do
little towards meeting the expenses incurred, but the Foundation is
fortunate in having wealthy backers. In 1939 it was financially responsible for a very successful expedition to the Garhwal Himalaya. This
year under its auspices one expedition went to Garhwal, and ours, for
which we paid, to the Gilgit region with the ambitious project of an
attempt upon Rakaposhi (25,550 ft.). One criticism I have of the Foundation, and it is shared by my two Swiss companions, is that it has a
weakness for publicity, especially for advance publicity. Quite apart
from the ethics of mountaineering it is bad policy. It is a rash marks-
man who calls his shots, announces which particular coco-nut he is
shying at—the wise man keeps his own counsel. So when going to the
Himalaya it is foolish to broadcast one's intentions, for after the event
it is not easy to describe an unsuccessful attempt on a mountain as a
mere reconnaissance.

Having received this tempting invitation before my own arrangements were completely cut-and-dried I was in a quandary; whether

to accept and thereby give up my own plans or to refuse and then possibly find that I had lost both opportunities. When presented with the choice of two evils one usually finds that one gets both. To have to choose between two proffered benefits is less frequent and more difficult; one never can have both and whichever one chooses there will always be a lingering regret after the other. To have one's cake and eat it, or to ride two horses (both with equal chances) in the Derby, are well-known examples of this particular vanity of human wishes.

In this instance, though the side-issues were many, the choice was roughly between mountain exploration and mountaineering on the grand scale, between something which might be of use by enlarging in a minute degree the sum of geographical knowledge and something which would be perfectly useless to anyone including the people who did it. A choice, too, between care-free license and reponsibility, for in the one there would be only myself and the Sherpas to consult and please, while in the other, as the only climber with Himalayan experience, I would be responsible for anything that might happen, good or bad. Mountaineering and mountain exploration are very much alike and in the course of an expedition the one frequently merges into the other. They might be compared to an omelette and scrambled eggs, the ingredients are precisely the same, one is perhaps a higher form of art than the other, and it frequently happens that what was meant to be an omelette turns out to be scrambled eggs and vice versa. To explore mountains one must climb and to climb an unknown mountain one must first explore. Perhaps the essential difference is that in mountain exploration strenuousness, hardship, and peril, can be increased or decreased at will, whereas in high climbing these present pains and retrospective pleasures are unavoidable. Their degree and intensity varies with the height and difficulty of the chosen mountain, but such things are then implicit in the enterprise and cannot be lessened or avoided without giving up.

Since a bird in the hand is worth two elsewhere my decision was made easier by the lack of any reply from Kashmir. Having delayed as long as politeness permitted I settled my doubts by accepting the Swiss invitation, which was no sooner done than permission arrived from Kashmir. By this time, late February, my friends had collected nearly all the equipment and food needed and I was asked to go to Zurich to cast an eye over it.

Without immodesty British mountaineers can, I think, claim to have had as much or more experience of high altitude climbing than any others; I was therefore surprised to find that in the most important matter of tents our experience had not been taken into account. The 'Meade' pattern tent (R.G.S. *Hints to Travellers* prefers the name 'Whymper') with a zip-fastener or a 'sleeve' door has stood the test of several Mt Everest expeditions and many others. For severe conditions of wind, cold, snow (not rain), it is hard to beat, and for simplicity, strength, lightness, is unsurpassed. But in Zurich they seemed not to have heard of it and had taken for their model a tent of French design, shaped like a coffin but of less simple construction than that article and far less easy to get into. One of the virtues of the 'Meade' pattern tent is its simplicity and its willing obedience and docility when being put up with cold hands in a high wind, whereas this Swiss tent by reason of having a fly and a sort of boudoir or ante-room at one end was unnecessarily complicated and difficult to erect or take down. The door fastenings, too, were not likely to be proof against driven snow, which will penetrate anything, even cloth if not tightly woven. For the good reason of economy the porters' tents, which are just as important as those for Europeans, had been borrowed from the Swiss army, but they were quite unsuited for our purpose. The material was thick and heavy, the poles were long, heavy, unjointed alpenstocks, while there was a door at either end secured only with buttons; one door in a tent is an unfortunate necessity, two are a disaster. Hannibal, I should say, or at any rate Napoleon, had probably used similar tents on their expeditions. For these I substituted a 'Logan' tent for the porters and took also three of my own 'Meade' tents. The 'Logan' tent I had first used with the Anglo-American Nanda Devi party from whom I had understood that it was a pattern designed and developed in Alaska, but it was not unknown in India for I read in *Hints to Travellers* that it was used by a Survey of India party in the Pamirs as early as 1913. Weighing only half as much again as the 'Meade', it holds four instead of two and is in many other ways as good.

It was impossible to quarrel with the sleeping-bags which were of real eider-down, so hard to come by now in this country, and were

Hans Gyr, Angdawa, Angtingit, Phurba, Robert Kappeler

Campbell Secord, Gyr, Tilman

The escort in the Kagan valley

Ploughing, Kagan valley

very warm and light. The rubber mats, which are used for insulation under the sleeping-bag, were thicker, lighter, and spongier than ours. This of course, is all to the good, but as their edges had been left unsealed they had also the absorptive capacity of a sponge which was all to the bad. The other items were all good and there was little to criticize except the variety and the quantity. Nothing had been forgotten except the great doctrine of 'the Minimum', taught and practised by one or two Himalayan pundits, but at Zurich regarded hardly at all, certainly not as inspired revelation not lightly to be departed from. The doctrine of 'the Minimum' is implicit in the name and is simply the logical expansion of the precept (which, by the way, is a Spanish proverb) that 'a straw is heavy on a long journey'. As I count myself one of these pundits, this was as great a shock to me as it has been to other prophets who have found their teaching ignored. Greater men, on less provocation, might have shaken the dust of Zurich from off their feet, but on the expedition I was in that embarrassing position of guest, or at least paying guest, in which it is not easy to set about one's host's furniture, throwing an armchair or an occasional table out of the window on the slender grounds of superfluity. However, I effected some trifling reductions, guaranteed to prejudice neither our comfort nor our cumbersomeness, and resigned myself sorrowfully to totting up the weights of the many packages—a list whose contents occupied some dozen sheets of quarto paper. It is a good working rule that an expedition that cannot organise itself on an ordinary sheet of notepaper, or, if all members are thorough-paced 'scrappers and baggers', on the back of an old envelope, is bound to suffer from the effects of too much organisation. That I had applied the axe very tentatively was evident when we reached India, when at Karachi, Abbottabad, and Gilgit, we left behind us a tell-tale line of dumps.

Crampons and skis were to be taken, though personally I have never had occasion in the Himalaya to use either. The crampons were made of some specially light alloy with ten short spikes. I suppose such things will always justify their awkward prickly presence as an insurance against the possibility of having to climb a long steep slope of very hard snow or a short piece of ice on the final bid for the summit. Anywhere below that level steps will always have to be cut to safeguard the porters who are not likely to have had the experience necessary for the use of crampons.

The use of skis for mountaineering in the Himalaya is a debatable point. They have been used on high mountains, I believe, only on two occasions. First on Kamet (25,447 ft.) in 1931 by Mr R. L. Holdsworth (an expert skier) whose use of them is alluded to in the *Himalayan Journal* (vol. IV) as follows: 'The use of ski by Holdsworth was fully justified. As far as Meade's Col (23,500 ft.) he was able to use them throughout the whole route with the exception of the rock face between Camps 3 and 4, and by ski-ing at 23,500 ft. he must surely have created a record for high altitude ski-ing. Furthermore, on the descent he was able to take his frost-bitten feet in one day from Camp 3 to the base, whereas others similarly affected, but not so fortunate, were compelled to drag them down in two long and tiring marches.' It will be noted that this benedictory paragraph while saying 'the use of ski was fully justified', says nothing of whether the carrying of them from Ranikhet to the mountain, a journey which took twenty-seven days, was also fully justified. In Mr Smythe's account of the expedition in the *Alpine Journal*, vol. XLIII, although the unregretted absence of raquettes is mentioned, there is no reference to skis except in the bald chronological summary at the end of the article. One cannot help feeling that if Mr Smythe had been impressed by the possibilities of skis for high mountaineering he would have remarked on it.

They were used again in 1934 in the Karakoram Himalaya by André Roch, a noted Swiss mountaineer who accompanied Professor Dyhrenfürth and his international cinema-mountaineering party. In their ascent of Baltoro-Kangri, or the Golden Throne (*c.* 23,500 ft.), he and his two companions used skis part of the way, and of this Roch remarks: 'Thanks to skis it took us only two and a half hours to reach a point which three days previously had been reached by our companions in five hours.' In conversation Andre Roch told me that at such heights it is impossible to use any other turn than a 'kick-turn', as 'stem' turns or 'Christianias' are too exhausting. But this is of small moment for, contrary to expectation, it is in ascending not descending that skis might be of value in the Himalaya. Provided the slopes of the mountain are not too steep and that one has confidence that they will be used and enough energy to carry such an awkward burden to the starting point, they should be taken.

In 1934 when Mr Shipton and I were in Garhwal, we did a high-level traverse from Badrinath across the watershed to Gangotri over the névé of several glaciers where we encountered snow conditions in which skis would undoubtedly have kept us somewhere near the surface instead of two or three feet below it; but then our three porters were also indispensable members of the party and more time would have been lost in teaching them how to shuffle along on skis, and of course in digging them out when they fell, than was wasted by floundering along on our feet. In the Karakoram, too, in 1937 when we were crossing the Snow Lake at the head of the Hispar and Biafo glaciers, skis would have added to our pleasure and enabled us to cover more ground; but for many weeks before that the carrying of them would most certainly have detracted from our pleasure and obliged us to cover less ground. But both these instances happened in mountain exploration, when one is necessarily accompanied by several porters, as distinct from high mountaineering. Such conditions could be met, I think, by an invention of Mr Seligman's (author of *Snow Structure and Ski Fields*) which anyone can use without previous instruction. What he calls his 'racket-ski' is about forty inches long and five broad, wider in front than behind, which helps it to rise to the surface at each step. Owing to their shortness and weight, which is only 5 lb., they can be carried easily on the back. They appear to be well worth a trial.

However, having seen some photographs of Rakaposhi I was confident that I for one, being no skier, would not be using them—not even Mr Seligman's—and I did my best to dissuade Gyr and Kappeler, who are both experts, from taking them. In this I not only failed but was persuaded in my turn to address myself seriously to the ski-ing business, for in Switzerland it is a business in every sense of the word. In that country, I imagine, a mountaineer who cannot ski is regarded with pity or with even something more derogatory. In a class apart from the votaries of the 'downhill only' school, are the ski-mountaineers who practise their difficult art not only in winter but in midsummer as well. Late in June 1946 I was the only ski-less mountaineer in the Bétemps hut where a ski club were holding a meet. From there they would climb the Lyskamm on skis, or all but the last few hundred feet of Monte Rosa, and then whistle down to the hut in some twenty minutes.

In vain I protested the inability of old dogs to learn new tricks—to Davos of all places I had to go to be put through the mill. Before this I had worn rather than used skis for a few hours in the winter of 1945 in the Dolomites, where I had reason to envy the partisans of Forno, a small village south of Mt Marmolada, who seldom wore anything else. To see them hurtling down slopes, dodging in and out of trees, in the middle of the night, while they collected the fruits of a widely scattered 'drop', was instructive and humiliating. In fact in winter snow three or four feet deep the valuable loads scattered over a wide area by errant parachutes would not have been recovered at all but for these men on skis.

The skiers at Davos were quite different from these, though they were no less skilful. To one accustomed in the main to unspoilt mountains the intrusion of commerce so high up their slopes subdued and desecrated with funiculars and ski lifts, the cafés with blaring wireless, and the ascending herd of overdressed women and men, breathing cigarette smoke into each other's faces in the train, was very depressing. Though, in fairness, I must admit that the sight of some of this same crowd descending in what seemed to me to be one suicidal swoop was no less encouraging and exhilarating. To Gyr and Kappeler, whose minds, no doubt, were casting forward to the execution of linked 'Christianias' on the slopes of Rakaposhi, the sight of their future companion's antics must have been equally depressing. Whilst I committed all the known mistakes and a few I had thought out for myself, they would circle round with encouraging cries. To a distant observer they must have appeared like hawks striking at a heron with a broken wing. The skis were duly taken to India, but as I have explained, skis in the Himalaya are no more indispensable than skates, and by the time Gilgit was reached my companions had seen enough to reconcile them to the truth of this. We had carried them far enough.

We were all fitted with specially made boots with the new type of moulded rubber sole which is becoming popular in Switzerland; many Swiss climbers, amateur and professional, seem inclined to change from nailed soles to rubber. Our boots were very stoutly made, perhaps unduly so, for my own size nines weighed nearly 6 lb. They took longer than usual to break in and the 'expedition' boots became one of our stock jests. I coined the aphorism that an extra pound on the feet is twenty pounds on the back, which though it may not be scientifically correct is a measure of how these boots felt to me. Nevertheless, leather is not wool and it is difficult to have warmth and strength without weight and on the whole these are the most essential qualities. A light pair of boots would be knocked to pieces in a couple of months. I think the rubber sole is very suitable for the Himalaya. With no iron in the boot the chances of cold feet and frost-bite should be lessened, while for boulder-hopping, which occupies most of one's time, they are supreme. They grip well on ice or snow, and though I thought they did not bite quite so well as nails when kicking steps in hard snow, this impression may have been a result of my own diminishing leg power. As regards their use in this country, except for the sake of hotel carpets, I should say that they are unnecessary and possibly a menace, since our rock is so often wet and greasy. One item of equipment new to me was a canvas boot cover reaching well up the ankle which, if well fitted, obviates the use of ankle puttees and keeps the boot dry even in wet snow, a benefit of the greatest value in the Himalaya where there are no drying rooms.

Formerly travel was undertaken to broaden the mind or to acquire culture, but nowadays many people go in search of food. I would not admit that this was our prime motive, but we took a keen interest in the matter as every member of an expedition should. In the exercise of this franchise there is seldom any slackness. Even the mountaineering mystics whom we sometimes read or read of, though they may not like to mention food, are certain to think of it. In 1947 the collection of enough food was, of course, impossible without the granting of special facilities, and it was consoling to find that the Swiss Government, which I had always regarded as a model of unobtrusive sense and efficiency, behaved in this matter much as any other government. Having with reluctance granted a permit for food for four men for five months, at the very last minute it occurred to some official with more perspicuity than his fellows that the loss of this amount might be detrimental to the four million odd Swiss who were not going on an expedition. Peremptory orders were therefore given that all our meat, all the butter, and half the cheese must be left behind. Fortunately our own food officials, with far more reason to be difficult than the Swiss, played up nobly and granted an export licence for enough butter and cheese to make good the loss. I also increased the amount of pemmican ordered. So many people ask what pemmican is that I might explain that it is a Red Indian ('Cree') word for dried buffalo or caribou meat prepared so as to contain the greatest amount of nourishment in a compact form. As made by them it consisted of the lean parts of meat, dried in the sun, pounded or shredded and mixed into a paste with melted fat in the form of a cake. It appears to keep indefinitely, has a high protein and fat content, and is expensive; it is the standard Arctic sledging ration, eked out with biscuit and chocolate. It is not the same thing as 'biltong', the sun-dried meat prepared by the Boers, or 'boucanned' meat from which the word 'buccaneer' comes. In the seventeenth century the island of Hispaniola (Santo Domingo) was the home of great herds of wild cattle which the natives used to hunt. The meat was dried in the sun without salt and cured in the smoke of a green wood fire. The adventurers who used to provision at Hispaniola learnt from the natives the art of 'boucanning'.

To-day we complain of lack of variety in our food but on Rakaposhi I could have borne with less variety and more solid simplicity. Many travellers, the Swiss among them, believe in the advantages of a highly organised system of food-boxes. In a generous but futile endeavour to please all tastes a little of everything—and the quantities are of necessity small—is put up in 50 lb. boxes, one of which is supposed to feed so many men so many days. Each box is neatly stencilled, with a list of the contents and the dose to be taken pasted inside the lid; and in severe cases of organisation the date and place where any particular box will be eaten is also laid down. The amount of each item being so small, the tins, jars, cartons are the more numerous so that in a 50 lb. box there is only about 30 lb. of food. Naturally, too, the most desirable things are soon spotted, so that by the end of a week one is left with a number of rifled boxes, like so many honeycombs from which the honey has been extracted and about as interesting. Not one of us ever contemplated, much less tried, living on a box for the stipulated number of days. It was the sort of experiment I should not care to see tried—even on a rat. The compilers of such boxes are like the compilers of anthologies, assuming seemingly that no one really knows what he likes, or that at high altitudes the mind is too sluggish to select and the body too feeble to pile the fruit of one's selection into a rucksack.

The Swiss were remarkable for their devotion to a food beverage with the sinister name of 'Ovosport'. They ate it dry, they drank it neat, and they even committed the solecism of mixing it with their tea. I always mistrust these food beverages which claim, amongst many other things, to quench thirst and satisfy hunger at the same time, for I submit that it is no more possible to do this than it is to blow and swallow at the same time. One eats soup and no one pretends he is thereby quenching his thirst; one drinks beer and no one but the brewer claims that he has therefore dined. Besides 'Ovosport' and other beverages of that type, without which health, strength, or even sleep are hardly to be expected, we had all the usual aids to comfort and well-being. In each box there were no less than twenty different species of food and over forty varieties, though since there was a whiff of the laboratory about some of them it would be more correct to speak of forty chemical combinations. As usual all failed of their effect; the Swiss had complaints ranging from boils to knee, stomach, and eye troubles; Secord, who will be introduced presently, suffered from a consumptive cough; while I had mountaineer's foot—inability at times to put one in front of the other.

Having thus equipped and provisioned the party I must shift the scene to India where our times of arrival were 'staggered' in the modern fashion. I reached Karachi by air on 1 May, the Swiss a week later, and Secord we were not to see until 6 June.

CHAPTER II

KARACHI TO ABBOTTABAD

A T KARACHI I FOUND that the Swiss consignment of stores had already arrived. Under a guard provided by the 'Stiftung' to prevent pilfering en route, it had been taken by road to Genoa and there shipped. 'Every writer of travels', I have read, 'should consider that, like all other authors, he undertakes, either to instruct or please, or to mingle pleasure with instruction'; for the benefit therefore of readers as ignorant as myself, I pass on what I learnt while we were discussing this question of shipment, namely that during the late war Switzerland maintained a merchant fleet and a port. The port was a quay and warehouse at Genoa from which coastal vessels plied to other Mediterranean ports. My share of our stores came in two ships, one of which arrived a day later than myself while the other was delayed at Bombay. This hitch was to cause us some trouble. Already the breeze of anxiety was playing around the brow of expectation, as it was to do frequently during the next three weeks.

Rakaposhi lies in the extreme north-west corner of India (now Pakistan) in what was until recently the Gilgit Agency. This comprised the petty states of Hunza, Nagar, Ishkuman, Yasin, Gilgit, Ghizar, Darel, and the Chilas republic, all of which were administered by a British Political Agent with headquarters at Gilgit. Gilgit itself was actually a 'wazirat' of Kashmir from whom the Indian Government leased it in 1935, although the Agency itself was established in 1889. These small states acknowledged the suzerainty of Kashmir but were never part of its territory. In August 1947 when the Gilgit Agency was hurriedly handed over to Kashmir, the Kashmir Durbar sent its own representative to Gilgit. This unfortunate, being a Hindu, was *persona non grata* and by the end of October was accordingly put in prison for his own safety. The states refused to be subject to Kashmir and declared their adhesion to Pakistan.

The usual route to Gilgit goes from Srinagar in Kashmir over the Burzil pass (13,99 ft.); another, about the same distance, avoids Kashmir and goes from Abbottabad by the Kagan valley and the Babusar pass (13,000 ft.). Both these passes are closed in winter for ordinary traffic but open about the same time in the spring in late May or early June. (The Gilgit mail-runners continue to cross the Burzil throughout the winter.) Col. R. N. Bacon, then Political Agent, Gilgit, had advised us to come by the Kagan valley route so that Abbottabad, which is railhead, was to be our starting-point. Coming out in the plane I had met as fellow-passenger Col. R. C. F. Schomberg, an old and very experienced Central Asian traveller, who having time after time begun his expeditions from Srinagar was concerned to find we were proposing to start from Abbottabad. There was no place like Srinagar for assembling and starting an expedition, for there, as he put it, 'you could buy anything from a set of false teeth to an ice-axe'.

However, having announced our route to the authorities we could not now change, so to Abbottabad I went on 8 May by train, along with twenty-four packages. To get this disgusting amount of stuff on a passenger train requires much local knowledge, and the Swiss firm Messrs Volkart Bros, readily put their ample stock of this commodity at my disposal. Arrangements had already been made for our four Sherpas, who were at Darjeeling at the other extremity of India, to meet me in Abbottabad on the 9th. As I had waited a few days in vain for my missing shipment I was already late, and the breeze of anxiety which had begun to play about me at Karachi, increased in strength and was presently to rise to gale force on account of these Sherpas.

Before I attempt to unravel and explain another complication in which we had landed ourselves, I must introduce the fourth member of our party, Mr Campbell H. Secord, who was, I think, in some ways responsible for it. As we shall see later he had been on Rakaposhi, or at least a ridge of it, in 1938, and as a pioneer, so to speak, had strong claims for inclusion in any attempt upon the mountain. Although he was working in a Government office his time was not his own, so that it was not until Gilgit was reached that we knew for sure that he would be coming. This important piece of news was brought by Secord himself.

To get to Abbottabad from Karachi one changes at Rawalpindi whence one goes on either by train or bus. Col. Schomberg had given me the name of a friend of his at Rawalpindi, a Maj. C. W. M. Young who is a keen traveller and an expert user of a cine-camera. Quite by chance, for I am not usually so longheaded, I had wired him of my arrival and given his name to Volkart. On Rawalpindi station at about 9 o'clock at night, as I alighted to look after my twenty-four packages, Maj. Young met me and handed me a telegram from the Government of India offering to fly* us and our kit to Gilgit for a consideration. So considerable was this consideration that I decided to stop the night, if not longer, at Rawalpindi to think it over.

Very early in our acquaintanceship the Swiss had been canvassing the idea of having ourselves and our kit flown to Gilgit. Our kit, by the way, would have to have been 'dropped' since the Gilgit airfield can receive only small planes with a load of about seven passengers. It was thought, however, that the R.A.F. in India might welcome such an opportunuty for an exercise, so negotiations, were opened by the 'Stiftung' with the Government of India through the usual channels. Secord, who at that time was toying with the idea of joining us, took up the flying project with enthusiasm, and since he had been in the R.A.F. during the war, where he had made some valuable acquaintances, he hoped he could pull wires to some purpose. After receiving an official reply to our application in rather discouraging terms we heard no more about it, and I mistakenly thought that the project had happily been consigned to limbo. But as the Chinese proverb says: 'Beware what you ask lest it be granted.'

The chief reason for this air-mindedness, of which I heartily disapproved, was the sound one that communal trouble at Abbottabad and in the Hazara district—then a very disturbed area—through which we had to travel, might prevent us starting at all. In addition the Swiss were anxious to save time, in particular Kappeler who regarded every day not spent in climbing as a day wasted. Perhaps such an uncouth method of approaching a mountain can be justified in a place like Alaska where the mountains are more inaccessible, the season shorter, and where the party itself has to hump or sledge the

---

*   In two planes—the bodies in an 'Anson' and the kit in a 'Dakota'.

Snow drifts below Gittidas

Snow drifts below Gittidas

Lulu Sar lake

Approach to Babusar Pass which is on saddle
near left edge of picture

gear. In the Himalaya I think the approach by air is a mistake. In the first place no one who wants to do a lot of climbing should go to the Himalaya where he will do very little. Secondly, the time spent on the approach march, be it only a week or as much as three weeks, is in my opinion time well spent. It may well be the only enjoyable part of the trip. One's body gets a chance to accustom itself to strange conditions and to acquire a little fitness: one gets to know one's companions and porters under conditions where the worst can be faced with manly resignation, whereas if some maddening habit or peculiarity was suddenly sprung on one when lying cheek-by-jowl in a tent with snow falling outside, the result might be manslaughter; and the porters in their turn have time to become familiar with tents and gear generally so that the place of everything is known and pitching and striking camp has become mere routine long before the mountain is reached.

And last, though I believe it should be put first, there is our old friend the 'thin end of the wedge'. I have quoted elsewhere the Bengali proverb that 'the sight of a horse makes the traveller lame', and I have some fear that the sight of an aeroplane might make the mountaineer think. To see an aeroplane accomplishing in four hours a journey which will take him nearly three weeks of toil and sweat is bound to give rise to thought—some of it subversive; whether the time so spent can be justified in the face of heaven and, perhaps, his family or employer; whether (unless he is a Fascist reactionary) it is not his duty to spare the oppressed coolies staggering along behind him their tribute of toil and sweat which his longer purse commands; or, still more to the point, whether it is not his duty to spare himself a little toil and sweat—a proposition which, of course, strikes at the very root of a mountaineer's religion. Such a picture is not entirely fanciful, and I have urged at length elsewhere* the case against the use of the aeroplane by Himalayan expeditions. 'Resist the beginnings' is a well-tried maxim. The farther away from mountains we can keep aeroplanes the better; a sentiment with which even pilots will not quarrel, and which, I hope, even those mountaineers whose pleasure it is to keep abreast or well ahead of the times will echo.

---

*   Everest, 1938.

It did not take me as long to make up my mind as I had expected. By the time Young and I had dealt with a large rump steak and a beer—in India even in the hot weather one must be uncompromisingly British—I had decided to refuse the offer without waiting to consult the Swiss. Perhaps I feared that Kappeler's eagerness to reach the mountains might overcome any desire for economy. Another beer encouraged a new train of thought—why not combine speed and economy by doing away with the 'Anson' which was to take our party of seven, and drop the bodies as well as the kit from the 'Dakota'? Any recalcitrance on the part of the Sherpas or the Swiss could be easily overcome if I had a good 'dispatcher' in the plane with me. On the other hand, what would my friends think of this *volte-face* after what I had said and written about dropping things on mountains; and above all, would the idea be as pleasing to the Swiss as it was to me, heated by rump steak and beer? After another bottle, alcoholic remorse set in. The cost of hiring the 'Dakota' alone would be the equivalent of one man's share of the whole cost of the expedition, the R.A.F. would probably insist on some preliminary practice in jumping during which someone might hurt himself, and in the end one of the Sherpas would get tangled up in the tail as he quitted the plane. This reminded me of the Sherpas. What were they doing whilst their unpunctual and heartless employer sat carousing in Rawalpindi? Sleeping under a bush in the garden of the dak-bungalow at Abbottabad seemed to be the answer to that. We finished our beer and sent telegrams to all possible sources of information at that place. Four men, I thought, with pronounced Mongolian features, one or two possibly with pigtails, should be conspicuous enough in this part of India; only later did I discover that Abbottabad was the station for a brigade of Gurkhas with many camp followers who were not in uniform, so that Mongolian features were perhaps the commonest of any, and that none of our Sherpas had pigtails.

Needless to say the replies to these telegrams were all negative and I naturally assumed that our men had not yet arrived. Indeed, this was the obvious explanation considering their long cross-country journey and the crowded trains, for at that time India was like an ants' nest into which someone had poked a stick. I therefore decided to wait for them at Rawalpindi where for the next few days I cycled to the station several times a day to meet all the likely incoming trains and to peer into every third class compartment—even into those reserved for women, for I knew the Sherpas to be men of resource. I recollected having gone through this sort of performance before, twice before in fact, at Sealdah station, Calcutta, and again on one hot dark night at Bareilly. Readers of Mr Shipton's *Nanda Devi* may remember our frantic and futile search of a train, our rushing back to our own train which was on the point of leaving, and our finding the missing Sherpas already safely ensconced eating oranges. Anyone who has seen a third class compartment on an Indian train will appreciate the task I had set myself. The usual description of sardines in a tin is pitifully inadequate because there the inmates are dead and lie in orderly tiers; a tin full of maggots gives a better idea of such a compartment because there, there is life and movement and all the vigorous competition which life implies as individuals fight their way to the surface to breathe. I became a familiar figure to the station staff and an object of curiosity to the habitués of Rawalpindi platform. All Indian platforms have a semi-resident population comprising the sellers of tea, the ice vendor (blocks of ice are his stock in trade, not ices), the fruit, curry, mineral water, and betel-nut merchants; the odd fakirs dossing down more or less permanently on the platform, and the sweepers who for a small consideration will raise a dust-storm in one's compartment from the dust which before was lying thickly but inoffensively on the seats, the floor, and one's belongings. For such as these my repeated visits and my harassed face became the cause of kind inquiries about my missing wife: from where was she coming; why was she travelling third class; and why had I left her behind?

On the 15th Gyr was due to arrive, the unlucky Kappeler having been left at Karachi to collect and bring forward my delayed shipment of stores about which I was beginning to feel not only worried but guilty. It was a nice thing if a representative of the Island race, a resident, too, of a great sea-port, was unable to ensure the arrival in time of a few paltry bales. What an ass I had been not to insist on their being shipped with the rest direct to Karachi instead of allowing them to go on a ship calling first at Bombay where anything might happen and apparently was happening. By this time I was heartily sick of Rawalpindi station and its curious denizens, so I decided to move on to Abbottabad to allow the Sherpas to look for us for a change. So on

the 16th we went there by bus and took up our quarters in a very indif-
ferent dak-bungalow. Once again all inquiries about the Sherpas drew
blank, while a wire to Darjeeling asking if they had started brought the
reply that they had left on the 4th—now, indeed, the brow of expectation was being blown upon.

Next evening as we were standing outside the Post Office, I was
accosted by an unmistakable Sherpa who proved to be Angdawa their
'sirdar' or leader. 'How long had they been there?' 'Six days'. 'Where
were they living?' 'At the Palace Hotel.' A twinge of anxiety on behalf
of the expedition accounts mingled with my relief. Four men for a week
at the Palace Hotel, the best in Abbottabad, would cost us a pretty
penny; but my fears were needless, for the bill, I think, was Rs. 3. They
must have slept under a bush in the garden after all.

Having introduced ourselves to the Deputy Commissioner, Mr
B. O. St John, we were invited to take up our residence in the comparatively luxurious quarters of the Circuit House bungalow which besides
being secluded had an ample veranda for our boxes and an empty
garage in which the Sherpas could be locked at night. The Deputy
Commissioner was having an anxious time and many sleepless nights.
During the few days of our stay there were unruly slogan-shouting pro-
cessions by day, and burnings in the Hindu bazaar and of outlying
Hindu temples by night, while occasional bomb explosions added to
the general uproar. The Moslem theory about these fires was that they
were started by the Hindu traders themselves, who having first insured
their stock set it alight and were thus free to depart unencumbered to
collect the insurance money at the other end.

Abbottabad is a hill station 4000 ft. above sea-level, about sixty
miles from Rawalpindi. It is the headquarters of the Hazara district
and is named after its founder Sir James Abbott who was responsible
for the settling of that wild district after its annexation to the Punjab.
He was Commissioner at Abbottabad from 1847 to 1854, but before
that, he had been the first Englishman to visit Khiva on the Amu Darya
in Uzbekstan. The only feature of interest at Abbottabad is a rock
inscription of Asoka near by which I am ashamed to say we did not
visit. But mindful of my mentor's remark about mingling instruction
with pleasure I might remind readers that Asoka (*c.* 247 B.C.) was the
great Buddhist emperor who was largely responsible for the spread of

that religion. His empire included all India, Nepal, Kashmir, the Swat valley, Afghanistan up to the Hindu Kush, Sind, and Baluchistan, that is an area rather larger than British India. Instead of interesting ourselves in archaeology we made the usual last minute purchases in the bazaar or what was left of it, walked the surrounding hills where pine trees gave us a zest for joys to come, and even visited Munsera by car in order to see the Black Mountain and some snow on a distant range. The Hazara district is like a tongue protruding from the N.W.F.P. for 120 miles in a north-easterly direction. It is bounded on the east by Kashmir, on the north by the outer Himalaya which separate it from Chilas, and on the west by a mountainous region occupied by the independent unadministered hill tribes of Kohistan, the Black Mountain, and others. It is not mountainous on a true Himalayan scale. On the Kashmir side of the Kagan valley, of which Hazara largely consists, the highest peak is Mali Ka Parbat, 17,360 ft., while on the Indus side there is nothing higher than 15,000 ft.

To calculate the number of mules required for an expedition is not so simple as one might think. Sometimes, if the mules have to be brought from some distant place the calculation must be done with precision, for a mule too many or even a mule only half laden, engaged at Rs. 6 a day is apt to give one a sharp pang every time one looks at it. It is simple enough to weigh all the loads and divide the total by 160, at the rate of two maunds of 80 lb. each per mule, but the loads, even to the last moment, are what an arithmetician would call a 'variable', and there is often some local custom which decrees that each mule must carry only one-and-a half maunds (120 lb.); or, as was the case between Chilas and Gilgit, two-and-a half maunds (200 lb.). An experienced man, an Angtharkay, for example, will take one look at a veritable tumulus of assorted loads and say at once so many mules—and, lo, it is so. The inexperienced will take paper and pencil and a spring balance, and when the mule train moves off he will be astonished to find two or three of his loads are still on the ground. On the whole it pays to err on the right side. The mule-men will grumble in no uncertain voice if their mules are overloaded, while any spare mule can always be handed over to anyone rash enough to ride.

Our mules were to meet us at Balakot, a place forty miles away near the junction of the Kunhar river, which flows down the Kagan valley, and the Jhelum, to which we were to take the loads by bus. We chartered a bus for this journey and, having ordered the mules, tentatively fixed the 22nd as sailing day. We only wanted a wire now from Kappeler giving his expected time of arrival, but before this came we received two others both of which rudely ruffled the placidity of life at the Circuit House. The first reopened the question of flying, which I thought had been settled, by advising us that 'the cost would be reconsidered'. This gave it a new and insidious gloss, for I suspected that the words might be interpreted as 'nothing at all', our descent on Gilgit having been in all probability arranged to take place under cover of a R.A.F. exercise. The eager Kappeler was happily elsewhere at this critical moment. Gyr, I found, was now lukewarm about flying, while I myself was positively stone cold. Moreover, our transport was now arranged, an advance had been paid, and we were to start in three days. To this offer we therefore returned a polite but firm refusal on the grounds that it was now too late.

The other wire came from Kappeler and although it called for no such bold decision caused me personally much more worry. It was to say that my Bombay argosy had at last arrived at Karachi but that one package of the seven was missing. This, I suppose, was not really suprising since the ship, instead of discharging at Bombay and coming to Karachi to load according to schedule, had decided to reload first at Bombay. All these seven packages were vital, not to me alone although one contained my personal kit, but to the expedition, for they contained the 'Meade' tents, the 'Logan' tent for the porters, porters' boots, sleeping-bags, and windproofs, and all our pemmican, and which bale contained what I had no idea. The firm that packed them had not provided any list of the contents of each bale and no bale had any mark of identification except my initials. All that could be done was to wire Kappeler that every package was necessary and that he must sit in Karachi until the tally was complete or until his patience and energy were exhausted.

The next news was from Young at Rawalpindi to say that he had fished the long-suffering Kappeler out of a train and that he had with him all seven packages. This came at lunch on the 21st. Our start was arranged for dawn next day for by now we were chafing to be off. Regardless of economy or Kappeler's feelings, for he and Young were both cine-camera enthusiasts and would have much to discuss, we hired a large car and sent it off with Gyr to Rawalpindi to collect the wanderer and the precious baggage. They were back that evening at dusk, Kappeler full of lurid tales of his experiences in the holds of the hell-ship *Historian* (for that was her name and by now that was what I thought of her), of the babus, stevedores, Custom's officials, and ships' officers, whom he had bullied and cajoled, of his despair and final triumph when he himself had lit on the missing bale lurking obscenely in some foetid corner of the hold, its sketchy markings obliterated with coal dust. I plied him with beer.

Far into the night Kappeler and ourselves did battle amidst a sea of boxes and bales in a way reminiscent of the scenes that must have been staged in the *Historian*'s hold, though now the stage, the Circuit House, was cleaner and probably not so warm. There was a lot of dunnage to wrestle with and many momentous decisions to be taken; whether we needed one shirt or two, two pairs of pants, three, or none at all; whether Gilgit should be gratified by our lounge suits or insulted with mere khaki. The despised and rejected had to be packed and transferred to the Commissioner's godown, fresh loads had to be made up and more weighing had to be done, the porters fitted with boots and issued with sleeping-bags, windproofs, and warm clothing—enough in fact to keep us up till midnight, and we were billed to start at 4 a.m.

With unusual forethought we had loaded the bus before calling it a night and turning in; but what avails forethought in the face of sloth? The driver, having carefully removed himself out of our reach overnight, returned only at 5 a.m., his head and face enveloped in shawls against the air of that unwholesome hour. We were off at last on our sixteen-day trek—nor were we mocked by the hum of any distant aeroplane.

CHAPTER III

THE APPROACH MARCH

———◆———

WITHOUT WISHING TO BE THOUGHT a self-righteous zealot I confess that I still find a dawn start fascinating. Heaven knows, during the war-years, there were enough of these to surfeit most people, while seamen or farmhands, for example, and thousands of workers going to work or coming off night-shift in winter, have every reason to view the very early morning with an indifference bordering on aversion. But the words 'start at dawn', which sometimes used to crop up in 'Orders' despite their unmilitary vagueness, invariably gave me a thrill of expectation. Possibly 'start' is the key-word rather than 'dawn', for it implies a move, an adventure, or at least a full day ahead of one.

Some writers of exotic stories would have us believe that east of Suez dawn is too abrupt to be enjoyed as we enjoy the lingering beauty of an English summer dawn. There they liken it to the drawing of a blind or even the switching on of a light, one minute it is black night the next it is full day. I have always found the several stages of an Eastern dawn long enough to savour fully each transformation. First, the stealthy transition from darkness to half-light, when mountains surprisingly resolve themselves into nearby trees and trees into clumps of grass, while the western sky momentarily darkens in contrast to the heightening pallor of the east; and then full light when the landscape falls into shape like the pieces of a puzzle; and at last the sun himself to dispel the lingering mists and to banish mystery and romance with his keen shaft of reality.

I have never forgotten a verse in a poem of the First World War although I have forgotten the author. His description of an Eastern dawn, or to be exact a Middle-Eastern, perhaps appealed more strongly because it was obviously written by a man who had served in a smart battery of Horse or Field Artillery:

How, when we went down Sparta way,
To sandy Sparta, long ere dawn
Horses were harnessed, rations drawn,
Equipment polished sparkling bright
And breakfast swallowed (as the white
Of Eastern heavens had turned to gold)—
The dogs barked, swift farewells were told.

The misery, ill-temper, and mistimed facetiousness of very early Alpine starts are forgotten and forgiven with the first hint of dawn, bringing with it a lessening of strain and restoring the mastery to eyes and feet. A new unimagined scene unfolds, affording the satisfaction of height gained and hours stolen from time. The renewal of well-being and kindly feeling which we had temporarily lost is partly attributable to our re-won ability to see and move freely on strange or difficult ground; but even when walking down a familiar street in the most commonplace surroundings the thrill of dawn can still be experienced, and possibly this is owing to our feeling that while others sleep we are the sole witness of the pageant of a new day, as if we were alone upon a newborn earth. De Quincey delighted in the silence and peace of early summer morning because—'Man is not yet abroad'.

However, when driving along a hill-road in an Indian lorry, dawn and the full glare of day cannot come too quickly. The scales are already sufficiently weighted in favour of a violent death without the added perils of the half-light. On our journey from Munsera we found the road only third rate and provided with enough hidden corners to keep one on tenterhooks even in broad daylight. No one who is in the habit of driving from the passenger's seat should undertake this section unless he is blindfold. But in the end we dropped down through the pines to the valley of the Kunhar without mishap and pulled up at Balakot rest-house.

The Deputy Commissioner of Hazara, in the midst of the prevailing unrest, had found time to deal with the additional worry of having us and our Sherpas passing through the district. One of his junior officials, a 'thesildar' who knew the people of the Kagan valley and who spoke good English, had been detailed to accompany us as far as the Babusar pass, and a local rajah had been asked to provide an escort.

The peaceful looking valley with its well-kept mule track, where people were too busy with their fields to notice us, did not seem the place to warrant an escort, but in the hills to the west there is unadministered territory from where, perhaps, trouble might be expected. It was possible, too, that the presence of our Sherpas might excite the Moslems of the valley. They are not Hindus, but are if anything Buddhists. Such a distinction would not, however, have been recognised by a Moslem at that particular time, for just as all cats are grey in the dark so anyone with a brown face who was not obviously a Moslem must be a Hindu and consequently anathema.

Our conductor, the escort of a dozen men headed by the local rajah, and the mules, were awaiting our arrival. The rest-house had been opened and breakfast prepared, so thither we adjourned leaving the muleteers and the Sherpas to wrangle over the loads. Just as letters will answer themselves if left quite alone, so at such moments if one avoids the scene of action for a sufficiently long time things will quite likely straighten themselves out. Our first sight of the escort suggested that it was in our honour rather than in our defence. Their most advanced weapon was an old single-barrel shot-gun while the rest defied classification. But at least there were no bows and arrows. However, Kappeler judged them sufficiently picturesque to expend an alarming amount of film.

On Bacon's principle that 'it is pleasant to see a battle from a distant hill', I lingered over breakfast as long as possible watching with one eye the scene of semi-activity in the compound. At the end of an hour five mules had been loaded, but as the march was to be short—the first day's march cannot well be too short—there was no cause for allowing angry passions to interfere with digestion. Patience, according to Buddhists is the greatest prayer. At last the loading was complete, though not before I had been compelled to accept one more mule, for my estimate though mathematically correct did not satisfy the mule contractor. In this case the 'variable' responsible for error was the presence among the mules of one or two dwarfs, but rather than wait to have them changed or to see them wilt under a full load I agreed to one more.

The mules filed out of the compound, the escort fell in, we were bidden to fall in behind, and off we went. We felt it unfortunate that

Map 2: The Approach March

the rajah took his escort duties so seriously. Except Kappeler, who was permitted to go ahead for cinema duty, we were not allowed to stray in front or very far behind, and the rajah was never really satisfied unless he had us all under his eye, bodyguard in front and we marching dutifully behind.

This year, as will appear, I was to have my fill of armed men. I do not dislike them as such in their proper place but I do dislike them in the Himalaya or in any out-of-the-way place where one goes in the expectation of solitude. If there are to be any people at all let them be 'the thing itself—unaccommodated man', not interlopers bearing arms or wearing uniforms who serve but to shatter the carefully fostered illusion that one has at last strayed beyond the last frontier. These sentiments are, of course, inapplicable to our harmless escort so thoughtfully provided and so kindly meant; nevertheless, without them my felicity would have been perfect. Just as so slight a thing as the wearing of a bathing dress detracts from the perfection of an otherwise perfect bathe, so the slight feeling of constraint marred the perfection of this long-looked-for return to marching and camping in the kindly valleys of the outer Himalaya. Still I felt uncommonly happy at trekking once more behind a string of mules with their bright headbands, gaudy red wool tassels, and jingling bells, over a road and country new to me with the promise of sixteen such days ahead. I felt I could go on like this for ever, that life had little better to offer than to march day after day in an unknown country to an unattainable goal.

Perhaps only a seeker after the Way who has attained those lofty realms where mind and thought are divorced from bodily feeling can hope to remain insensible to freshness or fatigue, hunger or satiety, cold or heat. The morning was well advanced and it was uncommonly hot, so that my thoughts underwent a gradual change. Far from wishing the march to go on for ever I did not care how soon it would be over. I did not care if it was my last. My companions evidently felt the same. They looked about feverishly for water and when we reached a stream one could sense the tremendous struggle between desire and prudence; for, no doubt, like most new-comers to India they had been warned that dysentry and death lurk in every river. Certainly on this day we cut a poor figure and qualified for inclusion among Carlyle's 'gluttonous race of Jutes and Angles lumbering about in pot-bellied

Indus valley near Rakhiot bridge looking south to Nanga Parbat

Same place looking north to Rakaposhi and Dobani

Rakaposhi from Thelichi

Rakaposhi from Chalt

equanimity; not dreaming of heroic toil and silence and endurance, such as leads to the high places of this Universe'.

We all have our theories about drinking on the march. I have always found it better in every way to abstain, which is not difficult if one is fit; for, as the Arabs say of the husbands of the talkative, 'great is their reward hereafter'. If one is not fit then a pebble in the mouth is a help provided that it is not swallowed. Others who should know adopt what appears to be the common-sense view and hold that the best way of dealing with thirst is to satisfy it; but I believe that it is not possible to do this while on the march, when one drink merely increases the desire for another, and that with thirst as with every other craving, 'to deny early and inflexibly is the only art of checking the importunity of desire'. On this occasion our self-denial was not severely tried, for Ahmed Sultan the thesildar, who was our cicerone, had arranged for a wayside halt where we were hospitably regaled with tea and maize bread, with a puff or two at a hubble-bubble for those who could use it. Maize bread is pleasant enough, once in a way, but its presence as a staple article of diet usually indicates a poor country where the peasants cannot afford to grow a much lower-yielding cereal like wheat. In Hazara, where land is scarce, it is the staple food as only the bigger landowners can afford to grow wheat. Owing to the dry climate the maize is a short-stemmed variety.

At 3 o'clock, hot, footsore, weary, we reached the Kuwai bungalow at a height of 5000 ft. Tea was ready and those who had denied themselves on the march reaped the full, exquisitely grateful reward of their abstinence. Below the bungalow there runs a small stream where I soon found a waterfall under which I could stand. I seemed to absorb as much fluid through the skin as I had done previously through the mouth. So great was my longing for this bathe that had the stream been more ample and its surroundings more gracious it would have qualified for a place in my list of 'memorable bathes'.

Kuwai was remarkable for the complete absence of flies, mosquitoes, ants, and similar noxious creatures. We dined outside in comfort. There were no flying beetles or moths to immolate themselves on the lamp or to drown themselves in the soup, and at night we slept outside on the ground without having to pick ants out of our hair or centipedes from under the pillow. When the mountain is reached 'sleeping out' loses its attraction, but on the approach march through the hot valleys I find it a great joy. As a prelude to sleep, reading in bed, though good, is not to be compared to listening to the restless mules, to the distant bark of a jackal, or to the wind in the pines. And while the fire glows red at one's feet one can watch the Great Bear take shape as one by one its stars rise over some black, jagged ridge, while Scorpion peers faintly over the mists of the southern plains.

There are eight stages along the Kagan valley to the Babusar pass, the exit from the valley over the Himalayan range at its head. Most of them are short or very short. This arrangement seems to be the most satisfactory, as no day is too short for the lazy or tired man and no day too long for the lusty or impatient, who, if he wishes, can do two or even three of these stages. But in a place like the Indus valley, for example, or the Karakoram pass route, where one must do twenty or more miles before finding shelter, grass, or even water, it is a case of 'Pike's Peak or bust' for all alike. Of course, if one is riding, the length of a stage is really only of concern to one's mount, but with a view to undergoing a 'hardening' process we made a point of walking all the way. It seems that in walking our standards, or at least mine, are far below those of the early mountaineers. Though I cannot trace the passage, I remember reading of a friend of Whymper's who was about to join him in the Alps, apologising in advance for bringing with him a young companion who through having been recently ill could not be expected to do more than fifty miles a day. I once walked forty-five miles myself, but I look on that as one of my more sensational adventures—as a man might who had once swum the Channel.

Our second march was more enjoyable than the first, perhaps because we were in a fitter state to enjoy it but probably because it was blessedly short. We left at 7 a.m. and were in by noon—a long enough time, too, for the enjoyment of scenery however fine. The track lay high on the left bank. Below us was the river running now over shallows in green and white foam, now swirling in pools of the deepest blue. Beyond, the forest swept up to the snow and rocks of Raggan Pajji and to the gentler summit of Musa ka Musalla (13,378 ft.), the Praying Carpet of Moses. Snow lends grandeur to the lowest and mildest mountain as a bearskin gives stature and fierceness to a Guardsman; in full summer when these mountains are stripped of their winter finery the valley must lose much of its Alpine character. The forests which grow freely on both sides of the Kunhar are worked for their timber which is floated down river to the Jhelum. Deodar cedar, blue pine and chir (*Pinus longifolia*), silver fir and Himalayan spruce, of which the last two are most common, are all used. On to-day's march we had our 'elevenses' at a timber contractor's logging camp where they were getting the felled timber down to the river which, as the snow melted, would soon reach its full height.

At Mahandri, twenty-five miles from Balakot, we were plagued with flies, while Kappeler in spite of his self-imposed water discipline had a bout of stomach trouble. Next morning we regretted our late breakfast when we found we had to eat yet another at a village half-way on the eleven mile stage to Kagan, for the lambardars, or headmen, were always eager to offer hospitality and help. Travelling under official patronage may involve constraint but it does ensure comfort and freedom from minor worries. At Kagan, at the far end of the gorge, our rajah friend and his escort left us, their place being taken by another local rajah with his retainers.

The new rajah was less of a martinet than his predecessor and his escort was smaller. March discipline was relaxed and our march to Naran, nearly 8000 ft. up, was the most pleasant we had had, for we were now getting high enough to be always cool. Naran was even more favoured than Kagan for arable land. There were many fields of dwarf maize, buckwheat, and barley, and water-meadows where the grass was rich and the flowers numerous; even I who am no botanist could recognise and welcome the blue and purple violets, light blue forget-me-nots, great white peonies, pink mallows, and yellow primulas. On this march we crossed our first snow-bed and the snow on the slopes of the valley appeared to come well below 14,000 ft., two facts which made our proposed crossing of the Babusar problematical—particularly as we heard a fresh account of its condition every day. We had been told at Balakot that there was no snow, at Kagan the road was reported blocked, and to-day we had met two lithe, picturesque looking hea then, who turned out to be Kohistanis, who assured us that the pass was open, for they had just crossed it. Still, as we were the first mule train of the year I was not confident; for snow upon which a man may easily walk may not support a laden mule.

Another difficulty presented itself. Apparently the flooring of the bridges on this route is dismantled in winter and stored; perhaps to safeguard it from the elements, perhaps to prevent it becoming an addition to the wood pile of some indolent villager; and now we had overtaken the road gang which was busy putting the road in order for the summer. From Naran we had boldly proposed doing a double march to Burawai, thereby cutting out a halt at Battakundi, but the road foreman objected to this because there were still two bridges this side of Burawai which had yet to be reassembled. With a little pressing he promised to make the two bridges ready for us and in return we graciously consented to take our day off at Burawai while he and his men laboured on the road beyond. This road foreman was admirable. He was a little shrunken Hindu of great spirit—foreman of a gang of Moslems in a Moslem country—and he drove his gang as if they were so many untouchables and he a high-caste Brahmin. No doubt when Pakistan became independent he lost his job, and possibly his life too.

We had another pleasant march to Battakundi. The road, still in woods and still on the left bank, followed close by the river which here flows peacefully in a wide bed, eddying quietly round rocky headlands and small islands all with their stand of sombre pine or fir. The thesildar promised us a dish of fish from one of these quiet reaches but the fish thought otherwise. 'The camel driver has his thoughts and the camel he has his', as the Arabs say. The bungalow, where we halted only for lunch, occupies the finest site imaginable on a grassy spur overlooking the river. In the distance were slopes of bare grass which now began to oust the forest, and on our right we looked up a side nallah to the magnificiently jagged wall of the 16,000 ft. Dabuka. During the eight remaining miles to Burawai the scene becomes wilder, the trees scantier, but the flowers more numerous than ever. We caught up the road gang, who had just put one bridge in order, and waited half an hour while they floored another over a side stream just short of the bungalow.

We were at about 10,000 ft. here, the weather was windy and unsettled so we slept inside for the first time since Balakot. Our day of rest which was cloudy, windy, and wet, we devoted to climbing a 13,000 ft. hill nearby in order to try out the 'expedition' boots. During the march each wore whatever he favoured. Gyr tried 'chaplis', the universal Frontier wear, and soon discarded them as I think do most sensible people. Since they act as a trap for stones and gravel and provide no support for the ankles, I cannot conceive why anyone should commend them, much less wear them. On a hillside, for which they are supposed to be the footwear par excellence, there is the further disadvantage that the foot, especially the heel, is seldom inside and overlaps the 'chapli' thereby becoming bruised and cut. Most natives wear them in the hills, though as often as not one sees them being carried, but since natives are quite at home with nothing on their feet and have never known what it is to wear boots, they can hardly be expected to realise the disadvantages. I favour plimsolls (the American 'sneaker') for the sake of their lightness on the feet or in the load, but their quality nowadays is not what it used to be. My first pair were finished before we reached Gilgit and my third pair did not carry me beyond Kashgar. On this 13,000 ft. peak of ours we encountered grass, gravel, rock and snow. We found that the rubber soles gripped well everywhere, but the boots themselves were damnably heavy and so stiff that our ankles were all chafed.

We were met here by a Chilasi with a letter from Capt. Hamilton, the Assistant Political Agent, Chilas, telling us that a party of Scouts would meet us below the pass and that a fresh lot of mules would be ready for us at Chilas. The next stage was to Besal from where after a conference with the road foreman we planned to cross the pass without the usual halt at Gittidas. Whereupon the foreman armed his men with long-handled shovels and hurried them on to clear the numerous drifts reported to him by the Chilasi.

Besal is 10,700 ft. up. Pines and birch in their turn had given up the struggle for existence, and even the hardy juniper bush was but rarely seen. The bungalow, too, as if in keeping with the barrenness of the land was bare of door or of windows—defects which caused our thesildar to mutter darkly about thievish Kohistanis. Close to the bungalow was a large circular platform of stones about six feet high; with a stone staircase, on top of which was a tomb, the whole beflagged with tattered bits of cloth mounted on long poles. The story was that this was the tomb of a very holy man who had come to Besal to pass the winter in solitary meditation, bringing with him as fuel for the long winter months one piece of wood. Not only had this provided the saint with fire throughout the winter, but when spring came there was still enough left to plant in the ground. Here it presently took root, sprouted, and in due time flourished into a noble tree. All this had happened within the memory of living man, but when we asked the thesildar where was the tree he replied that some sacrilegious pagan had cut it down and burnt it. Nevertheless, none of our men neglected to say prayers at the shrine of this holy man, and the thesildar was obviously stretching a point when he permitted us to mount the platform with our shoes on.

Forewarned of troublesome snow-drifts ahead we arranged to start at 5 o'clock, and by getting up myself to indulge in some indiscriminate kicking and cursing of sleeping forms we achieved a 6 o'clock start. For some such occasion as this I had with me a Swiss pocket alarm-watch—a gift from the 'Stiftung'. This went well as a watch but after giving me one or two successful calls it ceased to function as an alarm. Some two miles beyond Besal is the mountain lake of Lulu Sar which Kappeler with abundant energy had already visited the evening before for photography. This morning as we skirted its eastern shore he had further opportunity to catch the glories of snow and rock reflected in its passive blue waters.

We now began to find that all the side nallahs and re-entrants were drifted up in earnest, and the nearer we drew to Gittidas (11,860 ft.) the wider the drifts became. I cursed our late start, the mule drivers regretted it; for though a man could still walk on the surface the snow had softened so rapidly that the mules broke through at every step to plunge and flounder belly-deep. Here occurred our only serious loss, but since it more concerned our friends than ourselves we bore it with unexampled fortitude. We were carrying a case of whisky to our friends at Gilgit as a token of gratitude for benefits to come. The mule carrying it—evidently a Moslem mule with scant respect for this kind of white man's burden—in lurching himself violently clear of a drift, unshipped the whole load, and the case bounded off down the 'khud'. There was a merry sound of tinkling fragments, the eager nipping air became balmy with the gentle fragrance of whisky, and we realised that all was over and that our friends had sustained a very serious misfortune indeed.

Two miles away the wide pastures of Gittidas and the bungalow came in sight. It seemed to be occupied and presently lithe figures began running towards us. They were the Scouts from Chilas who had seen the plight of our mules. They threw down their packs and rifles and set to work with a will. Their lieutenant did not confine himself, as do so many officers, to the mere directing and encouraging of his men but worked himself harder than any of them, hauling at head collars, heaving on tails, carrying forward and readjusting fallen loads, and acting generally as a human bulldozer.

Under this welcome and compelling impact drivers and mules took fresh heart and in a short time we arrived at Gittidas where we dismissed with thanks our rajah, took the thesildar's photo and dismissed him also with thanks. Neither he nor the rajah would hear of any present, which was as well since I was armed only with presents for the Mirs of Hunza and Nagar. Once clear of Gittidas we found no more snow this side of the pass. Four miles away on a bare stony hillside, we could see the saddle and the cairn marking the summit. We reached this at 2 p.m. and should have seen, but did not, the mighty snow massif of Nanga Parbat thirty-five miles to the east, the giant before whom the peaks of our Kagan valley trip must bow their diminished heads, and far to the north, dominating all the Hunza peaks, the graceful Rakaposhi herself. There was no reason to linger. The Himalaya had been crossed, though there was little in our surroundings to impress the fact upon us, for between Nanga Parbat and the Indus fifty miles west of us, the Great Himalayan range droops, dwindles, and terminates for good. Nanga Parbat itself is an abnormality, for it does not lie on the main axis of the range but on a great buttress pushed out to the north, while in height it towers far above the main range itself. Another unusual feature of the Himalaya west of the Sutlej is that they are not pierced by rivers as are the Himalaya of Gharhwal, Nepal, Sikkim. The only way over them is by passes such as the Babusar, and the Burzil and Zoji in Kashmir.

On the north side there was still some snow, but a few hundred feet down it ended and there we found Capt. Hamilton awaiting us with an ample lunch already spread. By 4 p.m. we were down to 10,000 ft. again and close to Babusar village where we found the A.P.A.'s summer bungalow, the barracks for a company of Scouts, and a polo ground.

We were played in by the drum and pipe* band which any place of any pretensions in the Gilgit Agency maintains to welcome and later speed the guest, and to provide the essential musical accompaniment to polo matches. The match arranged in our honour was delayed by a thunderstorm during which we ate quantities of jam and scones in Hamilton's bungalow. The rain then ceasing and his cook and bearer, who were playing in one of the teams, having washed up, he donned white breeches, boots, and helmet, and we all walked across to the ground to begin the game.

As the reader will have guessed, polo in those parts is a democratic game. It is also the national game from Chilas up to Astor, throughout the Agency, and throughout Chitral too; and since it has often been described I need not waste many words on it. Essentially it is a game with few or no rules either as to ponies, players, or the size and shape of the ground. In these vertical valleys horizontal space is scarce and valuable so the ground is usually a long narrow strip, some 200 by 40 yards, with a low stone wall bounding the two longer sides. These walls have a dual purpose—as a stand for the spectators and as a cushion for the ball and the players. The space between the walls is usually grassy, sometimes stony, but seldom level. The six players of either side, not uniformly attired, on ponies not uniformly equipped, take up some sort of loose formation; the band strikes up, the less placid ponies prance and dance, the ball is thrown in by some distinguished guest (on this occasion myself) seated under a covered stand opposite the half-way line, and the game begins. Literally it is fast and furious. Hard riding, harder hitting, and no quarter given or asked, are its characteristics. When a goal is scored they change ends and the man who scored has the honour of what is called the 'tambok'; that is to say he gallops full belt up the field carrying the ball in one hand and when in mid-field opposite the distinguished visitors he throws the ball into the air and clouts it (if he can) towards the goal. Experts seldom miss the ball from the 'tambok' and quite frequently score a goal. There are no 'chukkas', but there is an interval at half-time, play each way lasting, I

---

*   According to Conway the reed-pipe is like a bag-pipe chanter. It has a scale of nine notes of the same intervals as the chanter except that the three upper notes are flat.

think, half an hour. I have seen only one or two of the more civilized polo games played on a vast acreage of ground, but as a spectacle I do not think it compares with this intimate wall game, with the squalling pipes, ponies and players in one constant mêlée, and the cheers and jeers of the crowd squatting on the wall on the very fringe of the battle. It sounds dangerous, and to me it looked dangerous, but Hamilton emerged unscathed from this long hour of peril and, as he wiped mud and sweat from his face, assured me that accidents were almost unknown. On the other hand, when I was at Kashgar, Mr Shipton told me that twice attempts had been made to start the game there but that on each occasion a man had been killed in the first few minutes. Anyhow I concluded that like Prince Hal's duel with Hotspur, 'you shall find no boy's play here, I can tell you'.

CHAPTER IV

GILGIT—ARRIVAL AND DEPARTURE

◆───────────────

From Babusar bungalow to Chilas is twenty-four miles, but the march is not so formidable as might be thought for it is down-hill all the way. From a height of 10,000 ft. the track drops steadily and steeply to 4000 ft. On this side of the watershed conditions are reversed; forest or vegetation becomes scantier as one descends, until near the bottom of the Indus valley it ceases altogether. On this day's march we stopped short of the starkest aridity for Chilas lies on a spur well above the main valley and is watered by a fine stream; indeed, in the garden of the A.P.A.'s bungalow the vegetation is almost tropically lush and various—giant blue gums and clumps of bamboo, mulberry and apricot trees heavy with fruit, walnut trees and edible pines. A warm shady oasis haunted by long-tailed paradise fly-catchers, hoopoes, golden orioles, and kingfishers from the nearby stream.

We were in by 4 p.m. and were soon reclining in long chairs screened by wire-netting against mosquitoes, eating without discrimination chocolate cake, mulberries, and apricots. Though our descent had been rapid the mules were not long in following. Last to arrive was Ningma, one of the Sherpas, who had been foolhardy enough to wear the 'expedition' boots. These boots preyed on my mind as their weight did on my feet; so much so that I sent a wire to Abbottabad for the porter's boots I had brought with me from England.

From below the junction of the Astor river with the Indus down to Jalkot on the Swat border the people are grouped in small communities inhabiting one or more nallahs, each community forming a separate republic. They constitute the area known as the Chilas subdivision of the Gilgit Agency and are administered by the A.P.A. stationed at Chilas village where there are also a fort and troops. Chilas was conquered by Kashmir in 1851, but when the British Agency was established at Gilgit in 1889 it was included as the Chilas subdivision. In 1892 a British mission was attacked by Chilasis and this led to the

58

Road to Nomal—typical Hunza gorge scenery

Rope bridge near Matun Das

View from Darakush to rock cirque at head of Manogar glacier

Gilgit Scouts at Darakush

occupation of the country and the appointment of a Political Officer at Chilas. This appointment was, I imagine, an enviable one; Hamilton's only complaint being the number of murder cases, the result of blood-feuds, which came up for trial. There is, however, a close season for murder when game like ibex, markhor, and red bear would be in season, and in addition there is trout fishing and polo. Right up to the time the British left India for good the life of a British official in the remoter parts was similar to that enjoyed by officials everywhere fifty years before. He was not tied to his office by ever increasing paper work, but was free to wander at will throughout his district, getting to know the people, learning where the shoe pinched, and amusing himself incidentally with rod and gun.

In accord with this well-tried method of administration Hamilton was able to accompany us to Gilgit, so that our march assumed even more the character of an officially conducted tour. Beyond getting myself from one stage to another I had no responsibilities. We paid off our Hazara muleteers and left at 6 a.m. next morning with a fresh lot of mules and ponies, the mules now carrying 200 lb., the ponies 160 lb. The Indus valley stages are long; moreover they are hot. The river lies at only 3000 ft., the air is dry, the sky cloudless, and the sun correspondingly fierce, so that the wayfarer trapped between the stark rock walls of the gorge is grilled like a herring suspended in a Dutch oven. The northern wall of the valley collects the heat and reflects it back to the opposing wall on the south bank. Trees which might afford a refuge from the sun or even grass upon which the eyes could find relief from the glare, are to be found only where man has tapped the life-giving water of some infrequent side nallah. Such places seldom fail to arouse admiration and astonishment—admiration for those who first had the enterprise and skill to make their homes on such an unpromising and uncompromising slag heap, and astonishment that water skilfully applied could overcome even that hideous sterility.

We marched on a stony track high above the river and instead of doing the brutal twenty-three mile stage to Jalipur halted for the night at Gunar where there is a Government farm. The principal crops are lucerne for fodder, and wheat, and while Hamilton went off on his tour of inspection we went down to the river. The slow moving dark brown canal which we had seen from the height of our stony track proved to be a fast and turgid river of great volume. Though it did not look inviting, not to bathe in the Indus would be an affront. But so fast and frigid was the water that all that could be done was to allow one's numbed body to be swept down for a short way and then scramble out and burrow a scoop in the hot sand of the beach. Though it was not what I would call a 'memorable bathe', yet it gave great satisfaction to bathe in so mighty a stream and to fancy that the water supporting one had come from the distant Mansarowar in Tibet or perhaps the great Baltoro glacier.

We dined in a mulberry grove off a savoury pilau in the strangest conditions. Almost as we took our places under a venerable mulberry, darkness having just begun, a violent thunderstorm with wind, dust, and a sprinkling of rain struck us. Men will go through fire and water on occasion for various reasons. In this case it was for the pilau. Like Lear we defied the storm. 'Rumble thy bellyful. Spit fire. Spout rain'—we might have declaimed—'but we will have our pilau.' So we put on coats, turned up our collars, clung to the table with one hand and shovelled in rice with the other.

Having only to do the six miles which we had left undone the day before, we reached Jalipur at 9 a.m. and breakfasted there. The bungalow was sited on a bluff round the foot of which the turbulent brown flood swept angrily. Upstream was a bay where it ran more calmly and here I tried my hand at washing the black sand for gold. Just across the river were the ramshackle huts of a family of gold-washers, but my choice of site was evidently poor for not the faintest trace of 'colour' in the pan rewarded my efforts. In the Indus in Baltistan gold-washing is an industry of some importance. So it is near Gilgit, particularly in the Bagrot nallah south of Rakaposhi which is said to be rich, and in many of the rivers of Hunza and Nagar. The usual time is in winter when the river is low; some families do nothing else, but they are driven to it by poverty and can only make a bare living.

This widely scattered gold must be brought from some reef or reefs which, one would think, it would be worth someone's while to seek. I have been interested in gold (and who is not) since my Kenya days when I spent six enjoyable and exciting months in vain efforts to find it. Prospecting, like many other attractive ways of making a living or near-living, is not the quiet, ruminative, ambulatory occupation of former days, when one went off into the 'blue' with a donkey-load of supplies, rifle, pick, shovel, dolly, and pan, chose a nice camp site near a stream and roamed the surrounding hills until the supplies ran out or one struck a Bonanza reef. Nowadays, I understand, sleek scientists consult their geological maps, are flown or driven to the chosen area, where, by peering into a box of tricks or listening through ear-phones they inform themselves or their employers with more or less accuracy what minerals there are several thousand feet below them.

From Jalipur to Thelichi is a very dry eighteen miles. Travelling in country like that of the Indus valley is best done at night or after a very early start. We were away by 4 a.m. in bright moonlight thus cheating, for a time at least, the crude hot day of its power to weary and dazzle. There is no better light to march by than that of a kindly moon—a quarter moon will serve—which, while revealing clearly enough the stones and pitfalls in the immediate path, hides discreetly the distant landmarks, cheating them, too, of their power to tease us with the slowness of our approach. By moonlight, too, is the best time to view, if one must, the bare bony nudity of our earth as disclosed by the Indus valley,* when the livid rock is transformed into black opacity, the hot sand into cool silvery greyness, and the dark river glistens.

We reached the Rakhiot bridge in time for a haversack breakfast. The Rakhiot nallah, the time-honoured approach to Nanga Parbat, joins the Indus at this point, where it flows in a narrow gorge, spanned by an iron suspension bridge. On the stone supporting pillar of the bridge are carved the names of the seven German mountaineers who with nine Sherpas were buried in the avalanche that swept over their Camp IV on Nanga Parbat in 1937. Far away, framed in the dark cleft of the Rakhiot nallah we could see the mountain itself glimmering white and high. From now on we were seldom without a snow mountain in view to which we could lift our eager eyes from the barreness on either hand. As we climbed out of the gorge on the right bank and the valley began to swing northwards, the whole vast face of Nanga Parbat came into sight, while at the third mile from Thelichi we had our first glimpse of Rakaposhi. There was no mistaking it. There was the high snow

---

* 'Mere crumpled Sahara', is Conway's apt description.

plateau on the western side which we had seen in the photographs, and there, too, was the graceful final pyramid to which the plateau served as a plinth. From the plateau to the summit alone was visible, and there seemed nothing there to arouse misgiving.

A similar early start on 3 June brought us to Jaglot* bungalow by 7 a.m. Here the A.P.A. from Gilgit (Mr Paul Mainprice) had arranged for us another polo match. Both he and Hamilton played, but we did not. I would not advise any mountaineer friend of mine to play any-where, least of all on this ground at Jaglot where the background or sight-screen to one goal is formed by the fluted ice and snow faces of Nanga Parbat while directly behind the other is the less majestic but equally distracting Dobani (20,126 ft.), an outlier of the Rakaposhi range. After polo came breakfast, and after breakfast a display of danc-ing to the same drum and pipe band which had recently been setting the polo ponies prancing. The dances are done by one or sometimes two men or boys. But here is no prancing. Violence and speed have no place, a slow graceful movement is the rule, more use being made of the arms, the body, and the head, than the feet, while the natural grace of the performer is helped by the flow of the long sleeves and skirts of his 'choga'. The dancer comes into the ring, gravely salutes the com-pany, and then turns towards the band with whom he seems to be in close communion throughout the dance. When done the company is again saluted.

After this we all took horse and instead of following the valley to Parri, our next stop, we went up the side valley of the Sai stream with the hope of the noble prospect of Rakaposhi which is sometimes obtained when coming back over the ridge between this nallah and the Gilgit river. Just above Jaglot the Indus valley strikes off to the east and the Gilgit river joins it from the north. We were disappointed of our promised view by cloud, but it was a pleasant ride in which Kap-peler, who had never been on a horse in his life, distinguished himself by staying on throughout. He did more. Unlike Captain Miserrimus Doleful who 'sat a horse with ease and grace until it began to move', he cut a very creditable equestrian figure even at a sharp canter. Parri is on the Gilgit river in which we must bathe to pay our footing. This river,

---

*   Not to be confused with Jaglot village at the foot of Rakaposhi.

like all the others at this time of year, was flowing fast, and the water was thick and discoloured. In winter when they shrink they become blue and limpid, and are then what all rivers should be, lovely to look at and friendly to swim in. A few years ago the P.A. Gilgit (Major Galbraith) and his wife were drowned in this river when their collapsible boat hit a rock and sank.

On 4 June we completed our final stage to Gilgit. We now experienced the truth of a proverb I have already quoted that 'the sight of a horse makes the traveller lame', for having now three horses, provided by Mainprice, at our disposal it seemed ungrateful not to use them. Moreover, having once tasted the joys of swift motion, effortless travel, the rush of cool air on our brows, the sparing of legs and feet, and the unnecessary saving of time, none of us was reluctant to taste them again. Between Parri and Gilgit, a matter of nineteen miles, the road is very suitable for riding, so much so that we covered it in little more than three hours. We drew rein but twice to peer hopefully up the Bagrot and Dainyor nallahs on the opposite side of the valley, condemning the first as being remote from our mountain and the second as being a too repulsive line of approach. But of that more presently. We received the kindest of welcomes from Col. and Mrs Bacon at the Residency where I was to lodge.

Gilgit township lies in the middle of what is for this broken country a large tract of flat easily irrigated land on the right bank of the Gilgit river near the junction of that and the Hunza river. In the whole of the Himalayan region I can think of no other township so surrounded by mountains. Within a radius of sixty-five miles there are eleven peaks from 18,000 to 20,000 ft., seven from 20,5000 to 22,000 ft., six from 22,000 to 24,000 ft., and eight from 24,000 to 26,600 ft. In a country so inimical to agriculture it is therefore, I suppose, a valuable prize, but compared with Kashmir, for example, one might well dismiss it as:

> ... a little patch of ground
> That hath in it no profit but the name.
> To pay five ducats, five, I would not farm it.

Nevertheless, many have considered it worth fighting for. In the first half of last century neighbouring rajahs quarrelled over it and there were five dynastic revolutions. In 1842 Sikh troops entered Gilgit and installed a garrison there. Then it was taken by the Hunza rajah and retaken by Dogra troops. Ten years later this Dogra garrison was annihilated and in 1860 Kashmir troops once more recovered it. In 1889, as we have seen, the British Government, acting as the suzerain power of Kashmir, established an Agency there in order to forestall any possible Russian advance.

Buddhist rock carvings—there is a good example at the mouth of a nallah two miles up river from Gilgit—suggest that this region was once the seat of a Buddhist dynasty, but nothing more is known of this and for centuries the people have been Mahomedans, either Shiahs or Maulais (followers of the Aga Khan). They are Aryans, and ethnologists call them Dards of Dardistan. They themselves would probably say that they were Shins living in Shinaka and speaking Shina. They are a likeable people though not so virile or so hard-working as their neighbours of Hunza and Yasin. Passing from a Gilgit village to a Hunza village one sees at once how much more skill and labour has been applied to the building and upkeep of terrace walls, water channels ('kuls'), and houses, and the consequently better state of the fields and crops. But superficially all these people, Gilgitis, Hunzas, Nagars, even Chitralis, look very much alike to the stranger. Their dress is a long woollen homespun coat reaching to the knees, pyjama-like trousers of the same stuff, untanned skin boots ('pabbus'), and the distinctive white or brown wool cap which consists of a bag half a yard long which is rolled up outwards at the edge until it fits the head. Those who are better off usually wear a 'choga' which is a loose coat-like dressing gown, embroidered, and with long sleeves. It is worn flung over the shoulders with the sleeves hanging empty. This garment is more commonly worn in Chitral, and in Afghanistan the 'chapkan', as they call it there, is almost universal. The dislike of putting one's arms inside sleeves is not merely a habit of the lazy East, but is common in Albania and in Italy.

The little township of Gilgit (4800 ft.) is attractive, well planted with trees, the fields and houses pleasantly intermingled, and the stone walls of the fields are bright with sorrel. Unlike most Indian stations there is a blessed absence of corrugated iron, so useful but so ugly. This is not unexpected when one considers the distance and the awkward mule-load such sheets would make. Barracks for the Gilgit Scouts, bazaar, hospital, court, and some half-dozen houses for European officials make up the sum of buildings. Only when a caravan arrives from Kashgar does the bazaar show much life. About six of these a year come down from distant Kashgar, bringing with them principally felt 'numdahs' and salt. One arrived when we were there and with it were two delightful Swedish missionaries who had been obliged to quit their Kashgar mission on account of Moslem prejudice.

Having arrived on the 4th we decided to leave on the 8th, so we had little leisure. Reorganising the loads, arranging transport, and buying all the necessary stores, kept me busy; while the kindness of our friends would not allow us early nights, for upon each night of our stay we had an engagement to fulfil. In spite of our mishap with the whisky there seemed to be enough to drink, and when the imported article ran out there were local resources to fall back on. A small amount of wine, rough as a rasp, comes down from Hunza for friends of the Mir, while one or two of the residents had manfully attempted the distillation of apricot and peach brandy; indeed, if alcoholic content is any criterion, success had been achieved, for some we sampled was mere bottled lightning. Bottled mulberry juice in large quantities was available for those who did not wish to char their insides, or might be taken as a lenitive by those who had already done so. Gilgit and fine fruit are synonymous terms. Were I going again I should pay more attention to making my arrival coincide with the fruit season, and should this happen to be the best time for climbing the mountain—well, so much the worse for the mountain. But only the apricots were ripe, and they I found palled after a few days gluttony. The mulberries—large as bantams' eggs—the peaches, apples, and pears were not ready.

Any spare time I had was spent either in the swimming pool, or in whittling away odd slices of rubber and leather from my 'expedition' boots to reduce their weight—a futile proceeding prompted by the same futile hope with which a drowning man clutches a straw. Still, I was face to face with the fact that our start was imminent, that in a matter of days I should have to drag this weighty handicap up many thousands of feet, and that no amount of apricots or apricot brandy would make the task any lighter. It was also high time to decide finally on a plan of campaign.

Rakaposhi lies about twenty-five miles to the north of Gilgit on the east side of the Hunza river.* According to the report of the Karakoram Conference, which was held in the winter of 1936 with the object of clarifying the range-names of the Karakoram, Rakaposhi lies on the Rakaposhi range and is the outstanding peak of what is called the Rakaposhi group. It is the only peak of the group which has been triangulated and its height is 25,550 ft. The naming of Himalayan peaks is always a matter of difficulty. Either the regions round the mountain are uninhabited or the natives are too uninterested to name individual peaks. If a peak happens to be so awe-inspiring as to demand christening then those living on another side might give it a different name, so that the early and possibly ignorant traveller is given two names both of which he probably takes down wrongly. There is thus still scope for originality on the part of later travellers, but in due time one name becomes generally accepted and later appears on a map. This is the signal for interested linguists or ethnologists to step in and practise their science by suggesting alternative spellings or interpretations of the name. Monographs have been written on the correct spelling of Kangchenjunga, while the Tibetan name for Mt Everest, Chomo Lungma, the spelling of which also occasioned a number of quarrels, has been given a great variety of meanings. Similar confusion surrounds the name Rakaposhi—its meaning and even its original language. 'Devil's Tail', the first meaning ascribed to it, has long been exploded; more probable is 'Raka's View-point', Raka being a mythological character who once climbed the mountain with a strong party of fairies; but Conway's interpretation is much less poetic, for he was told that it meant 'like the white matter exuding from a boil'—Raka, perhaps, was subject to boils. But the Hunza and Nagar people, who live closest of anyone to the mountain, settle the matter by calling it Dumani which means 'Necklace of Pearls' or 'Necklace of Clouds'. However, the Karakoram Conference plumped for 'Rakaposhi' (refraining from any attempt at elucidation) with the proviso that the Hunza name 'Dumani' should also be retained or at least not quite forgotten.

---

*   See sketch map on p. 77.

Fortunately for the reader the mountain is almost without history. Lord Conway (then W. M. Conway) explored the Bagrot nallah in what was for Himalayan climbing the almost prehistoric year of 1892. In his book *Karakoram Himalayas* he describes how his party climbed the ridge between the Bagrot and Dainyor nallahs and looked down on to the Dainyor glacier 'and up to the highest point of Rakaposhi on our right. We noticed that the great, though from here strangely insignificant-looking mountain, could be ascended by the arête which is a long gentle snow crest apparently not corniced. The only difficulty is to get on to it, for the wall leading to it was entirely avalanche-swept from end to end.' It is not very clear to which arête he refers, but it is probably the south-west. The mountain is not heard of again until 1938 when Messrs Campbell H. Secord and J. M. K. Vyvyan explored the approach by the Jaglot nallah. They climbed a peak at the western extremity of the north-west ridge which in their account (*Himalayan Journal*, vol. xi) is given as 22,500 ft, but which from our experience I should say is not more than 20,000 ft. From here their advance was stopped by a steep drop of 700 ft. to the ridge and by the unpromising aspect of the long icy knife-edge stretch of ridge which followed. It is not very clear why so little interest should have been shown in so noble a mountain, why such a high and glittering prize seen by so many travellers and so easily reached should not have been snatched at before. At first I attributed this neglect to the 'eight thousand metre' fetish which beset nearly all Continental climbers in the 1930s, when any mountain which failed to reach this lofty standard was despised; but now having seen the mountain myself I think there were sounder reasons for its immunity from attack.

Even at this comparatively late hour in its history Himalayan climbing is still in that rude, happy, and despicable stage when no one looks for a hard way up a peak if there is an easy one, when there is no need for the aspirant to glory sternly to ask himself whether or no his chosen objective is difficult enough to test his skill, courage, and luck, but whether it is easy enough to offer a chance of his climbing it. And, of course, the higher the mountain the easier it must be to offer him that chance.

On this fairly slender basis of fact and with the uncertain help of some photographs we had to make our plan. At first it seemed that the soundest method would be to reconnoitre every side of the mountain beginning with the Bagrot nallah, then over into the Dainyor by way of Conway's saddle, from there round to the Jaglot nallah, finishing possibly with the north face. On the march in this idea was modified. In the first place it would take a long time, although until we came to reconnoitre the Jaglot approaches none of us fully realised quite how long so wide a reconnaissance would have taken. To split up into two parties of two (or two and one since we did not yet know whether Secord would come) would not have been satisfactory because the Swiss had no Himalayan experience and we had no common standard, so that to compare and settle the respective merits of routes recommended by either party would not have been easy. Moreover, our time was short. I had arranged to leave for Kashgar by the end of July, when Secord's time, too, would be up, and if we were to reconnoitre three widely separated nallahs and possibly the long northern face there would be little enough time left for the climb itself.

On the march between Parri and Gilgit we were impressed by the distance between the Bagrot nallah and the summit, while the Dainyor nallah, in giving us a brief but horrifying glimpse of little else than ice and rock-walls, also gave us good reason why it should be ignored. As for the north side, Secord had seen that and had written it off as too steep—a view which the photographs confirmed. So by the time we reached Gilgit we had practically decided to gamble on finding some way up from the Jaglot nallah. According to Thucydides, 'it is a habit of mankind to entrust to careless hope what they long for, and to use sovereign reason to thrust aside what they do not fancy', and though we did, perhaps, overmuch entrust ourselves to careless hope in the matter of the Jaglot nallah and readily thrust aside the alternatives which we did not fancy, we happened, I think, to choose or guess rightly.

Meantime, on 6 June, returning to the Residency from shopping in the bazaar, I stumbled over a vast, strange rucksack on the veranda and concluded at once that Secord had come. He had left London the previous Sunday and here he was in Gilgit on the Friday. He may have been lucky or he may have had even more influential friends in the R.A.F. than we knew; for that morning Col. Bacon had gone by air to a conference in Srinagar, and whether the plane which brought one and took away the other had been arranged for Secord's particular behoof or for the Resident's was a nice point which, with its implications of relative importance, I should hesitate to decide.

Having been told of our plan Secord concurred heartily since he was more confident than we were that the Jaglot nallah offered not only the best but our sole chance. There remained, therefore, only the job of finding the necessary porters to carry two months' supplies to the head of the nallah. Col. Bacon himself had already begun negotiating by telephone with the Mirs of Hunza and Nagar for a dozen likely men, but the Mirs, anxious to do their best for their subjects, had stuck out for a rate of Rs. 3 a day and food. As this was the rate we were paying our Sherpas, serving a thousand miles from their homes and doing more than merely carrying loads, I thought it too much, so that when the Commandant of the Gilgit Scouts told me that some of his men were keen to accompany us and that he was willing they should, I jumped at the offer. Volunteers were called for, and almost all responded to the call. From them we picked fifteen, who, in the short time showed great powers of marching and load-carrying and a ready cheerful obedience. These local levies of the Gilgit Scouts, smart on parade and with a very military bearing, are organised in platoons on a tribal or territorial basis—a Hunza platoon, Nagar, Gilgit, Yasin, and so forth. Of these we were told the Hunza platoon was the pick. It seems a pity that such a fine well-trained body of men should not have been given the chance of proving their fighting worth during the late war. I think they would have given a good account of themselves and I am sure the peace of Gilgit would not have been broken in their absence.

So at last we were ready; loads made up, mules for the first day's march to Nomal engaged, and the last heart-rending decisions—two sweaters or three, Shakespeare or Charles Reade—irrevocably taken. Our last party was attended and our last farewell said at midnight against what some hoped and others feared would be a 3 o'clock start.

CHAPTER V

THE JAGLOT APPROACHES

◆

THE SEVENTEEN-MILE STRETCH of road between Gilgit and Nomal is in local opinion the worst stage in the Indus valley. The road is in many places buried in sand and there is no oasis of greenery or even a solitary tree to break the monotony of sterility. The only water is at one point where the road approaches the river. In summer, at the height of the melt, these big rivers have the colour, consistency, and temperature of pea-soup which has been burnt and then iced, but the local people drink it with avidity. Just as some prefer a wine with plenty of body, so I noticed Hunza men purposely avoiding rills of clear water in favour of the thick river water. The hot dry march in front of us was therefore one very good reason for such an early start, and through the devotion of Mrs Bacon's servants, who got up to give us breakfast, we were spared 'the heaviest stone which melancholy can throw at a man', which, according to Fuller, is to learn that there is no breakfast. But although we were all on our marks by 4 a.m. three of the mules had wisely absented themselves, so that it was not until an hour later that we got away with five donkeys as substitutes.

However, except for the air-borne member, the party was now fitter, and with the help of a bathe (where there was no temptation to drink) we made lighter of the march than we had expected. For the last three miles the road winds through the pleasant rice and wheat fields of Nomal, for the bungalow is placed at the far end of the village. It seems to be part of the natural perversity of inanimate objects like bungalows that they invariably place themselves at the most inconvenient end of a village or on the highest ground available. For a week or so we were to be accompanied by Mr Mainprice, whom we had already met on our way to Gilgit, who had a matter to discuss with the elders of Jaglot village. He caught us up at Nomal late that night along with Gyr who had chosen this inopportune moment to have an outbreak of boils which had had to be treated at the Gilgit hospital.

Camp on right bank of Kunti glacier (13,000 ft.) looking to its head

Camp on south-west spur (17,000 ft.); see also frontispiece

The corridor route: Summit upper left corner,
Monk's Head right centre, rock 'island' below and left,
in centre of picture

At Nomal the mules returned, for on the next march the Hunza river had to be crossed by a rope bridge; all loads therefore had to be made up into man-loads. We determined to be off at 5 a.m., and so we should have been had my pocket alarm-watch been working. Some fortunate people will guarantee to be awake at a given hour, and so can I but only by dint of lying awake most of the night. If you wish to rise at four, for example, you simply think hard of the figure four and tap the forehead four times repeatedly to advise whatever there is inside of your intentions; but this unseen mentor often seems to be unable to count, and having woken you up at 1, 2 and 3 o'clock, without any activity resulting on your part, gives up in disgust and allows you to have your sleep out undisturbed. So it was at Nomal, but as we were sleeping outside we sensed the coming of dawn so that our start was but an hour later than intended.

Two miles from Nomal we left the main Hunza road to cross the river by the rope bridge—one of those contraptions which has struck fear into the hearts of many travellers and which has in consequence been often described. Our natural inquiries as to its condition received the usual assurance that it was very rotten, not having been repaired in the memory of man. I have yet to hear of one of these bridges breaking or even, which seems the more likely event, of anyone falling off. On this particular bridge there was the usual deep sag in the middle, the usual thick cables far too thick for a real 'Thank God' handhold, and the usual grey flood surging angrily below. I have never tried, but I have been told that if you incautiously allow the eyes to rest on the water too long the bridge begins to sail rapidly up stream. Then anything may happen—either complete catastrophe or more likely the victim is paralysed, like a rabbit by a stoat, and clings on helplessly until rescued. The Swiss crossed without hesitation although such bridges were outside their experience. Not so the Sherpas, who cut poor figures, all except Phurba having to have their loads carried over, while the sirdar Angdawa had to be carried by one of the Scouts.

Some eight or nine miles above the bridge the track strikes up the hillside away from the river, and after a steep climb of several hundred feet debouches quite suddenly upon grass meadows and fields of ripening wheat where channels of water were bubbling merrily downwards. A mile further up the nallah were the willows and apricot trees

marking Jaglot village (8000 ft.) and beyond the glorious but deceit-
fully foreshortened Rakaposhi. We reached the village by noon expecting that after lunch the march would be resumed. I was not so sure,
for I knew of old the symptoms indicative of 'thus far and no farther',
and true enough both Scouts and Nomal coolies declared that for their
first day they had had enough. None of us, I imagine, regretted the
wasted but blissful afternoon spent lying on the grass in the shade of
the apricots, the fruit of which one might with a little trouble catch
as it fell; least of all Gyr who was not at all well because of his boils. I
had leisure to discover what had been left behind—medicines was one
item—and still worse what we had forgotten to leave behind—a useless
mess-tent, for example. This halt gave us the opportunity of making
bread and scones, and having once shown Angdawa, who doubled the
role of cook and sirdar, we seldom went without bread in the lower
camps. Chapatties are good enough in their way, but I pride myself on
supplying bread whenever possible. With 'atta', dried yeast, the ordinary aluminium 'degchi', and a wood fire, it needs no great conjuror to
turn out a loaf in a short time; a much better loaf, too, in my opinion,
than that which we eat at home, not unfairly describable as 'a deleterious paste mixed up with chalk, alum, and bone-ashes, insipid to the
taste and destructive to the constitution'. Thus Smollett describes the
bread of his day and if in place of 'bone-ashes' we read 'calcium and
other fortifiers' the description is still pretty accurate. Nevertheless, it
seems likely that since successive generations have put up with such
bread for 200 years they will go on putting up with it to the end of time
or until their constitutions break down altogether.

The next day's march involved a steady climb of about 4000 ft.
The lambardar of Jaglot accompanied us to show the way, bringing
with him the princely gift of two sheep for which we had to pay. Mainprice remained behind to look at the crops and to harangue the elders
who were not seeing eye to eye with him in the matter of a new water
furrow ('kul') for irrigating some land in the main valley on which
Mainprice was eager to see some Hunza folk settled. The Hunzas, who
are far and away the best agriculturalists of these parts, suffer from a
shortage of land. This new 'kul' was to be taken from the Jaglot stream
in which there seemed to be water to spare, but the Jaglot elders were
properly jealous of their water supply.

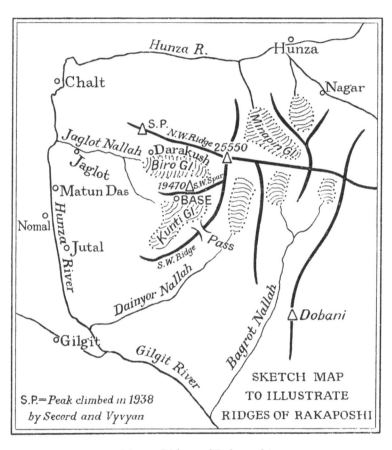

Map 3: Ridges of Rakaposhi

A thousand feet above Jaglot is the last permanent habitation, the small hamlet of Barit. Beyond that we mounted steadily through pines until at about 11,000 ft. we left these behind and emerged on to the high lateral moraine of the Jaro glacier. At this point the Jaglot nallah divides; the arm in which this glacier lies runs up between the north-west ridge and the south-west spur of Rakaposhi, while the other is contained between the south-west spur and the south-west ridge. We followed the right-hand moraine of the Jaro Gamuk ('gamuk' means glacier) until at about 12,000 ft. we quitted the moraine for the ablation valley between moraine and mountain side where there are two grassy alps, a lower and an upper. The upper alp called Darakush is the better of the two and had been Secord's camp site in 1938, but to-day, since the Scouts with their heavy loads were lagging behind, we camped in the lower at 3 p.m. As these alps and the slopes above them are grazed by the cows of Jaglot and Barit we enjoyed for the first week our daily milk. It had a peculiar flavour of sage, the result of the beasts eating a herb (which I cannot name) which grows everywhere in these parts. When Mainprice arrived he exerted his authority to have the cows confined to a diet of sweet grass, of which there was enough growing in the two alps, whereupon the milk became much more palatable. In 1938 Secord had here been so plagued by flies that at Jaglot he had suggested that cows should be prohibited while we were camping there; but quite apart from this being a rather high-handed order I felt that the presence of flies was preferable to the absence of milk.

From the top of the moraine we had had a good view of the north-west ridge and the ice-fall of the Jaro glacier. Almost on a level with the Darakush alp the glacier bends gradually more to the east and begins to rise moderately steeply in an extremely broken ice-fall. This part of it is known as the Biro Gamuk. Remembering what I have said about early or ignorant travellers hearing or taking down wrongly what they are told I record with diffidence the names given to us. It is unfortunate, too, that there should be different names for parts of the same glacier, Jaro and Biro, but at least they are short, unlike the name Conway was given for a peak above Baltit—Boiohaghurduanasir. The multiplicity of names is common in the case of rivers, every few miles of which may have a different name.

We had not made the important decision to concentrate all our efforts on the Jaglot approaches merely to try once more the north-west ridge which Secord had already condemned; nor had we come here entrusting ourselves entirely to careless hope. On the contrary, our hopes were founded on many close inspections of Secord's well-thumbed photographs and now we were in a position to see what these were worth. Examining mountain photographs over a restaurant table after a good dinner with a view to route-finding is like playing Snakes and Ladders and about as useful; the ladders by which one climbs swiftly to the top of the board are so obvious while the writhing snakes of Pride, Anger, and Covetousness which compel one to start afresh are readily overlooked. Secord had condemned his ridge on account of the difficulties at its beginning, and I must admit that here the photograph did not flatter it. The south-west spur, which is inaccessible from the Biro side, did not look any more promising, but the ice-fall on the other hand, appeared in a photograph almost inviting. It was upon this then that our hope mainly rested. True the upper part was hidden, for our scientists (bless them) have not yet invented a camera which can see round corners, and most of the visible portion was endangered by the ice-walls and hanging glaciers which menaced it from both sides. But in the absence of anything better our hearts had warmed to this route in spite of such deterrents to affection. We argued that the worst of ice-falls must yield to time and patience and that by sticking diligently to a middle course in the traditional British way we might find safety. Both these theories were subsequently found to have flaws.

Having now had the ground in question in view for the best part of an afternoon I confess our hopes were a little dashed. But the length and exposure of both the north-west ridge and the south-west spur gave the ice-fall route added attraction, although even at such a distance we could see how broken it was and how little, if any, appeared to be completely free from danger from above. In the Himalaya, avalanches and the discharge of séracs are often on a grand scale and will unexpectedly sweep across large areas of even flattish ground. Still, the ice-fall route would at least be more sheltered from bad weather than the ridges. The climbing there, however, slow and intricate, would be neither difficult nor dangerous for our inexperienced Sherpas, and

3000 or 4000 ft. up there was a convenient rock 'island' which might serve as a base. We determined to try it.

The mention of weather recalls to me that by now we had complaints to make on this score. When Secord was here in July 1938 he enjoyed a month of hot cloudless weather, tormented only by flies, and I had been firmly of the opinion that in Gilgit rain was almost unknown. In the few days we were there the weather had been neither hot, cloudless, nor settled, and though we were assured by the residents—as one always is—that such conditions had never been known before, the fact remained that they existed then. Up in the mountains we might expect worse and in this expectation at least we were not disappointed. Our first day was cloudy with much wind higher up; in the evening it rained, and early next morning there was a heavy thunderstorm.

The Scouts were sent back to Jaglot for the rest of the loads while we climbed over the moraine, dropped down to the glacier, and started up it to see what we could make of the ice-fall. It proved to be a good deal more broken than Secord's camera had thought, and after 500 ft. we were brought to a stand. Disregarding our avowed intention of steering a safe middle course we made wide casts right and left but without success; seracs, ice-cliffs and crevasses running criss-cross in all directions completely baffled us. This was all the more annoying and unreasonable since the angle of slope was less than thirty degrees. In thoughtful mood we returned to camp where we devoted the rest of the day to moving it to the higher and more favoured site at Darakush.

A better base camp in every respect but one I have yet to see—a flat roomy carpet of short grass, through which a stream meanders, surrounded and sheltered by birch trees interspersed with great boulders, a few of which afford dry and ready bivouacs. And the alp is so situated that while reclining on the grass one may look out from this perfect setting to the summit itself, to the long flat north-west ridge, to the broken heavily-corniced south-west spur, and beyond the foot of this to a fascinating cirque of rock and ice precipice at the termination of the south-west ridge.

The one serious drawback to this camp is its lack of height, for it is somewhere between 12,000 and 13,000 ft. On most big mountains one can usually achieve a flying start from a base at 17,000 or 18,000 ft. to which the local porters can carry without difficulty, but to attain even this modest height on Rakaposhi usually involved some serious climbing. All the valleys here are exceptionally low, taking their cue from the Hunza river into which they drain. To the north and west, where it almost washes the foot of Rakaposhi, the river runs at a level of only 6000 or 7000 ft., and the northern slopes of the mountain drop from 25,000 ft. to this level in less than seven miles. Still, this is an imperfect world and we were too content with our surroundings at Darakush to worry much about the lack of height. We sat about outside that evening watching a herd of ibex at the foot of the north-west ridge, while a wan and watery sun fitfully lit the highest snows. Rain fell most of the night.

We were not quite finished with the ice-fall. While one party tried to find a way round by the right bank, I took Phurba with the intention of making a very high and wide detour on the slopes of the south-west spur. Mainprice, with his rifle, accompanied the first party intent on murdering an ibex; while Gyr, who was still convalescent, had chosen that moment for a quiet stroll along the top of the moraine clad in a dazzling white suit of windproofs. When after a careful stalk Mainprice gained his point he was chagrined but not surprised to find that the ibex had taken the hint.

Phurba and I had a successful day. After climbing for a thousand feet up loose rock and steep grass we crossed a wide bay of snow and dropped down again to the ice-fall which at the edge here was much less broken. Stones fell intermittently from a black cliff on our right and obviously the snow bay was sometimes swept by avalanches, but otherwise the route seemed safe. At 2 p.m. we reached the rock 'island' at about 16,000 ft. This rock refuge in the ice-sea lay close to the edge of the ice-fall which out in the middle was proportionately more contorted and convulsed than below. Even if it was possible further progress would be slow and difficult, nor could we yet see what lay round the corner a thousand or more feet higher where the glacier bends south to articulate with the south-west ridge. While we were climbing we had seen a large avalanche pour down from a big snowfield on the slopes of the north-west ridge and out on to the lower part of the ice-fall, and when we returned to Darakush at 4 p.m. we heard how the other party had come well within its fell whiff and wind. A local man who was with them had only avoided being caught by it by a short head. They, too, had seen an avalanche fall into our snow-bay after we had crossed and were in consequence less enthusiastic than they might have been over our having reached the 'island'. Owing to ibex and avalanches they had not gone far up, but anyway their route was unpromising since to reach the 'island' they would have had to cross the ice-fall.

Sitting over our curry and rice that night, lamenting the saddle of ibex that might have been and cursing Gyr for its absence, we faced the facts and came to the reluctant conclusion that the 'corridor' route, as we called it, had not been fairly presented in the photographs and that it had better be left alone. 'Corridor' was an apt name; it was narrow, it undoubtedly led somewhere, and like other corridors, the Polish for example, it was subject to interference from either side.

I have never made a proper study of mountain photographs. Perhaps if I had I should not have received so many unpleasant surprises as I did on Rakaposhi. On the other hand, it may have been sound instinct which made me regard such photographs rather cursorily, for there is no doubt that they conceal as much as they tell and that as guides to route-finding they are unreliable. I am not blaming the camera; the human eye is no less fallible. Slopes which appear innocuous from below are found by experience to be horrifyingly steep, while others which when viewed *en face* look like vertical walls turn out to be veritable belvederes. On Rakaposhi these illusions were frequent. In one instance, even a slope viewed in profile—a view which admits no deceit—appeared far less steep than we, having climbed it, knew it to be. No doubt my scientific friends have an explanation for this as they have for everything, but in the end most of us are content to believe what we see.

Having thus rejected the 'corridor' route we had but three shots left in the locker and one of these we expected to be a misfire. While the 'corridor' had been falling into disfavour some of us had been casting rather wild despairing glances over our left shoulders at the north-west ridge where the searching eye of faith thought it could see a way of gaining the ridge at a point well on the summit side of Secord's difficulties. He, it will be recalled, was stopped by the steep drop from the peak at the west end of the ridge and by the long knife-edge section below it. We could see that the great snow-field—almost a hanging glacier—from which yesterday's avalanche had fallen to so alarm the 'corridor' party, swept down unbroken from the crest of the ridge at a point half a mile on the summit side of the knife-edge section. It was guarded on the near side by ice-cliffs, but if we could reach it and if the angle did not prove to be quite so sharp as it appeared, then there seemed a very fair chance of reaching the ridge at a most advantageous point. For the ridge was certainly the shortest and most direct way to the plinth or plateau on which the summit pyramid stands. Except for one harmless-looking rock step and one snow cupola, which could be turned, it was apparently devoid of difficulty.

There were undoubtedly a lot of 'ifs', and Secord for one had little faith, so before wasting time there we decided to look at the other arm of the Jaglot nallah where there were two unexplored possibilities, the south-west ridge and the south-west spur. Again it rained all night and we started late for our day excursion round the foot of the south-west spur. We crossed the dry ice of the Biro opposite our camp and walked down a pleasant valley of grass, birch trees, and clumps of wild roses, lying between the left-hand moraine and the slopes of the spur. We turned the corner and climbed a long boulder-strewn slope to the moraine of the Manogar glacier. The splayed-out foot of the south-west spur must be nearly two miles in length and at the upper end of it the Manogar glacier is joined by another branch, the Kunti glacier. This lies between the south-west spur and its parent south-west ridge, and from the junction with the Manogar to the head is not more than three miles. The upper part of Manogar flows in almost the opposite direction to the Kunti. It arises in the great rock cirque at the curving tail of the south-west ridge and then sweeps down towards the foot of the south-west spur. But as Byron said: 'Damn description, it is always disgusting.'

Our interest lay up the Kunti so we walked out on to the glacier well beyond the foot of the spur. There was no ice-fall to block our view and we could see it sloped gradually upwards to its termination under an extremely steep and broken wall below the junction of ridge and spur. Two miles up the glacier the snow-slopes of the south-west ridge to our right looked as if they might afford a way to the crest.

The upper part of the ridge leading to the great plateau seemed very broken, but we thought it had possibilities. Accordingly the next move was to bring a light camp round for a thorough reconnaissance.

Next day, 14 June, we moved round with two Sherpas and six Scouts to carry the loads. Instead of going out on to the glacier as before we climbed the broken moraine on the right bank, keeping close under the cliffs of the spur. As we toiled up a thunderstorm broke, bringing with it rain, hail, and then snow, so we were obliged to camp sooner than intended at the first available trickle of water. The height was about 13,000 ft.

After lunch we continued in knee-deep snow up the glacier to within half a mile of its termination, and the more we saw of the south-west ridge the less we liked it. The slopes leading to it, which from a distance had looked attractively easy, now looked steep and difficult. There was much argument about their angle; some thought it not more than 45°, others a great deal more, but whatever it was the ridge itself was not sufficiently encouraging to induce us to go and find out. Turning our backs on this we searched the slopes of the spur and here at any rate there seemed a ready access by way of a snow gully not very far from camp. From Darakush we had had a good view of this ridge in profile, and from photographs we knew it abounded with pitfalls, but as it seemed to be the only accessible ridge we decided to give it a trial. We walked slowly back down the glacier in snow showers and sunshine, our sense of indecision only slightly alleviated.

The south-west ridge and rock cirque at head of Manogar glacier

On the south-west spur looking back to point, 19,470 ft.

South-west spur with gendarme beyond the 'horn'—furthest point
reached—marked ✕. Summit at back; Monk's Head slightly right of ✕;
north-west ridge and 'plateau' to the left

CHAPTER VI

THE TWO RIDGES

———◆———

O NCE MORE SNOW FELL THAT NIGHT SO, instead of climbing the gully, we made a short excursion to the great cirque, partly to see if a low rock col leading to the Matun Das nallah south of the Jaglot could be crossed, and partly to get a view of our southwest spur. On this upper part of the Manogar glacier we had to climb an ice-fall to reach the cirque, beneath which we presently stood, gazing up respectfully at the grim grey slabs shot with streaks of yellow rock and festooned with long glistening slivers of ice. From a closer view-point the col looked difficult (later Secord and Kappeler were repulsed by it), but we had a clear view of our spur and beyond it to the summit. At the point where the spur bends sharply at the head of the Kunti glacier to articulate with the main south-west ridge there is a high snow-dome, guarded near the top by an ice-wall below which a steep crevassed snow-slope falls away to a low gap. This feature became known to us as the Monk's Head and was evidently a major obstacle.

That evening at supper I introduced the Swiss to pemmican soup by way of warning of what they might expect higher up. There were no delighted cries, no hearty lip-smacking appreciation. In fact of Gyr one might have said that he:

> Sighed, as he chewed the unaccustomed food:
> 'It may be wholesome but it is not good.'

The refrain 'snow fell all night' is becoming a rather monotonous dirge, but once again the fact must be recorded. Leaving the others to ponder over pemmican and the weather I walked round to Darakush to arrange for the remaining loads to be brought up. Angdawa had been left there with Angtingit, our fourth Sherpa, who had some kind of fever, together with the Scouts in charge of their Subadar. The latter were now due to return, so as we had at last made up our minds to explore the south-west spur we had to move our base camp before they went. Mainprice having already gone back, taking with him his rifle, the Subadar had beseeched me to get him one; for the ibex by now had forgotten the horrid white apparition which had walked the moraine a few days ago and were again grazing in provocative proximity. On his strolls the Subadar had been tantalized by the sight of so much fresh meat walking about, and he had no doubt often exclaimed as the old Boer did: 'God, what things a man sees who goes out without a gun.' Believing that he knew something of the game and that he would not blaze away indiscriminately, I had sent a Scout back to Gilgit with a chit asking for a rifle. It is worth noting that the man did the double journey within two days.

When I arrived at Darakush I was told the Subadar was up the hill after the ibex and while I was devouring fried eggs and chapattis I heard a shot. 'Good', I thought, 'he's got one'. But to my horror this was immediately followed by four more in rapid succession and after a brief interval another two. I blushed for the Subadar, and for myself at having let such a miscreant loose upon the hill, for it was clear he had not killed with his first shot and had tried to mend matters by the grievous sin of firing away at the running herd. That this had happened I heard next day when he came up with the Scouts and proudly presented us with the leg of a diminutive buck. One undersized animal killed and three wounded was the tally, but my Hindustani was not fluent enough to paint the enormity of his crime.

By the time the Scouts arrived we had moved our camp up 200 or 300 ft. to some grass off which the snow had recently melted. Unlike Darakush this camp was neither silvan nor pastoral, but it had the advantage in height by nearly a thousand feet. For wood we used to send the Sherpas down to the foot of the spur where some gnarled juniper bushes grew on the cliffs above. Having settled in here with all our stores and gratefully dismissed the Scouts with a reward, we were ready to launch a fresh blow; but the unsettled weather and the amount of snow which had recently fallen admonished us not to launch it too violently.

On the 17th we set off for the gully. Quitting the moraine above the camp the way led up a broad fan of soft snow through which we ploughed until we reached the rocks at the foot. To the top there must have been 2000 ft. of snow-filled gully, the lower half of it very soft and deep; nor was there any escape from the snow to the rocks on either side, for they were too steep and rotten. The gully itself was much steeper than we had bargained for. Once more our judgement had been confounded by experience. Good judgement is, perhaps, the most valuable of all mountaineering assets, and whether our own was deficient or not we took comfort from a dictum of Dr T. G. Longstaff, an old Himalayan traveller and now President of the Alpine Club, who declared that in the Himalaya one must first rub one's nose in a place before being able to say whether or no it will go.

We reached the crest of the ridge in five hours from camp. Later journeys only took four hours, but to-day we had the exhausting work of treading out steps. Kappeler seemed to be going well, Gyr and I slow and steady, but Secord was obviously suffering from a too sudden transition from office desk to mountain. A notch at the top of the gully made a convenient camp site, roomy and flat enough to permit the digging of platforms for several small tents. On one side a big rock gendarme forbade any movement along the ridge in that direction, while on the summit side a snow-slope rose steeply for a thousand feet, blocking out any further view of the ridge. We judged the height to be something over 17,000 ft. That day there was not much to be seen, but later we enjoyed many noble prospects from our eyrie.

The gate now seemed open, or at any rate the latch was off, but instead of rushing at it like bulls we took a day off. A plan had to be made and loads arranged to conform to it. We decided to put a camp at the notch with tents for ourselves and two Sherpas, and stores and oil for a week. From there we would push another camp as far as we could along the ridge from which two of us could explore further—as far as the Monk's Head we hoped. The morning of our off day was delightfully fine and sunny, so much so that Secord, who has a salamander's passion for the sun, exposed almost every inch of an extremely long body to it. By evening wind and hail had driven us to crouch once more in our stone 'sangar'.

When we went up next day everyone carried loads, the two Sherpas, Ningma and Phurba, had about 40 lb. each and ourselves 25 lb. The steps of the previous day were a great help so that in spite of our loads we reached the notch in four-and-a-half hours. With 'Bernina' shovels we dug platforms for two small tents and the Logan, and having pitched these we went down. Another carry the following day with food and personal kit was done in four hours with only one short halt at the foot of the gully. We kept Phurba and Angtingit with us and sent Angdawa and Ningma down with instructions to do another carry next day. It was obvious that neither Phurba nor Angtingit had ever camped on snow before, for I had to put a Primus stove together for them and show them how it worked. Although this was but one day off Midsummer Day and although the camp was at no great height, no snow was melting on the rocks so that to get water we had to use the stoves. We had with us as well two shiny black squares of light oil-cloth which given enough sun and enough time would collect sufficient heat to melt snow; but such a source of supply is pretty meagre. Secord was out twice in the night crying loudly for water, perhaps in the hope that the black cloth squares also functioned by moonlight.

So far the Sherpas have not had much notice. Angdawa, the sirdar, was reliable and efficient either as headman, porter, or cook, and he could also interpret fairly successfully between two people speaking different languages neither of which he knew. Angtingit, bovine, cheerful, tremendously strong, with the chest of a gorilla and with a facial resemblance to one of the more refined, was afflicted on and off with sickness and finished up in hospital. Phurba, young, shy, but anxious to please, was the most typical looking Sherpa of them all and the most likeable; while Ningma, with the appearance of a slightly battered veteran, was unluckily without a veteran's experience—at least not in mountaineering, though by his looks he had had much experience of life. He was afflicted with a smoker's cough, but in spite of my reiterated advice to abstain (which he probably thought was not disinterested) he always clamoured the loudest for his cigarette ration. He was the weakest member of a not very strong quartet, and as the emptiest barrel so he resounded the most. They all did their work, but they had little or no experience of climbing and seemed somewhat averse to enlarging the little they had. Their war-time experiences, either in some labour corps or with English and American service people touring Sikkim, seemed to have opened their eyes, particularly Angdawa's, to the main chance; whereas, before the war one had the impression that the pleasure and success of an expedition were of far more importance to the Sherpas than the reward. But that is a criticism which, perhaps, few of us can escape; for Darjeeling, or even remoter Solah Kombu, is no more immune to the shrivelling economic blast than anywhere else, and to thrive in times like the present greed must become greedier and generous carelessness must e'en sharpen its wits.

A gloriously sunny evening, on which we stood around outside watching the shadows lengthen across the face of Nanga Parbat far away to the south, gave no hint of the weather to come. Morning broke cold and dull with a rasping wind from the east; no one seemed eager to leave his tent and no Sherpa appeared with kind inquiries about breakfast. Since the stomach carries the feet I got up and heated and broached a large tin of sausage, but by the time we had eaten them there was no sign of improvement in the weather. Loth to give up we started unladen up the snow slope hoping to see something of the ridge higher up. We climbed through steep and deep snow with occasional patches of rock showing through until after an hour's climbing the angle of slope began to ease off. We were near the top of the ridge at a point marked on the map as 19,470 ft., but by now mist and sleet were driving across reducing visibility to a few yards. There was no obstinate contest of disagreeable virtues. With one consent we turned to hurry down to the notch whence, in order to save kerosene, we retired to the base. On the way down we met Angdawa and Ningma coming up with loads and a parcel of mail, dried apricots, and tobacco from Gilgit. All the dried apricots of these parts are good, but these were a special sort with the kernel of the nut wrapped in the dried fruit, a present from the Mir of Hunza. Down below a thunderstorm raged, and when it had passed we made bread, chewed apricots, smoked, and felt better.

In the Alps where time is usually of the first importance it is difficult to sit still during a spell of unsettled weather, but in the Himalaya where time is measured in months rather than in weeks there is no reason for impatient activity and every excuse for complete idleness. Instead of lying at earth as we should have done, we kept on carrying loads to the notch, so that when we reoccupied the camp we had there enough stores to mount a full scale attempt, although we had yet no idea whether the route would really go. The weather was behaving very oddly. I have never experienced so many thunderstorms in the Himalaya where I have always regarded them as rarities. On a fine morning the Swiss, two Sherpas and myself, made another carry. We found that the snow in the gully had avalanched, obliterating all our steps, not only those in the gully but also those right down to the bottom of the fan. While it was agreeable to learn that this had taken place in our absence we had the less pleasing thought that next time we might not be so fortunate. In the afternoon there was more snow and thunder—an odd mixture—so next day we stayed at home to give the snow time to settle.

An idle hour could always be spent in a treasure hunt in the food boxes where something might have been overlooked, or another more careful translation (by Secord) of the German on some strange packet might rouse fresh hope or at least stimulate curiosity. One of the more disquieting aspects of the American way of life has been taken up by the Swiss. What are called cake, pudding, or pancake 'mixtures' are put up in packets (no doubt sterilised) in some hygienic food factory, so that all the modern housewife need do is to apply water and fire.* For supper that evening we tried a pancake 'mixture' with a thick dressing of dried banana flakes to ease it down. It was not a dish to be eaten on one's knees, and the banana flakes, I thought, closely resembled glacier sludge.

On the 24th all, less Ningma who was sick, went up to the notch with more food and a load of wood. We cleared the snow off the tents, dug out the buried stores, and squared up generally. The weather was very different from that of a week ago; summer seemed to have set in at last and 300 ft. down the gully we found a trickle of water. What lovely and memorable pictures were painted for us that evening while the setting sun crowned the distant Nanga Parbat with a halo of bright gold and drew dark indigo shadows upon the white cliffs; while the tangle of snow peaks to the west, too lowly to be crowned, stood out cold and sombre above the turquoise haze of their valleys. Just as from some Cumberland crag we search for distant Snowdon or Snaefell, so here, not content with Nanga Parbat, we saw or thought we saw Tirich Mir 150 miles away in Chitral.

---

*   The self-heating tins which we met with occasionally during the war will save even that, for she will merely have to apply her cigarette end to the tin.

June 25th was another fine day and a critical one. Our plan was still to push a two-man camp along the ridge, so when we started at 8.30 a.m. the Sherpas, Phurba and Angtingit, were carrying about 30 lb. each and ourselves 15 lb. The snow was in good condition and in two hours we had reached what we took to be the point marked on the map as 19,470 ft., though no amount of tapping could persuade our altimeters to confirm this. We had two of these instruments and their readings agreed like brothers, but they seemed to feel the effects of altitude less than we did and usually lagged behind by a thousand feet or so. From this point the ridge stretched away almost horizontally. It was heavily corniced and in the distance it seemed to terminate in a horn overhanging space like a question mark. We climbed on two ropes with a Sherpa in the middle of each. Gyr, who was now leading my rope and apparently allowing ample margin for the cornice, suddenly broke through it with his outside foot and a large chunk of ridge disappeared. I was thankful to see that even without much help from his second he was able to retain his status quo and his equanimity.

As we drew nearer the question mark assumed a more questioning shape, reminding me somehow of a rhino horn viewed from a flank—such as would qualify for inclusion in Rowland Ward's *Records of Big Game*. With one accord we dumped our loads. By midday we had reached the foot of the horn to find it guarded by a spacious crevasse bridged in only one place, on the very crest of the ridge. There we had lunch—'a full belly and then to business', as the Duke of Wellington used to say before battle.

It seemed to be my turn to lead, at least no one else pressed his claim, and having crossed the bridge (a frail link, I thought) I was able to appreciate the full beauty of the route. The northern side of the horn consisted entirely of vast cornice curling out over space on our left, while the convex side was so arranged that if one took too high a line one would fall through, and if too low then one would equally obviously fall off. On the passage of the horn itself there was no question of kicking steps, the snow was so deep and soft that I had to shovel with both arms and with great labour carve out a sort of communication trench. Some mild protests on my part were drowned in cries of encouragement from behind. At last the concavity straightened itself out and having rounded the horn I stepped on to the gap

beyond it, a move which brought into view the startling drop on the
north side which previously had been hidden. Ahead, along 200 ft. of
loose knife-edge rock covered with snow, the ridge ran up to the tip of
another gendarme. Phurba, who was behind me, having taken a quick
look into the abyss and to the knife-edge along which we should have
to balance, remarked sensibly enough that he was going back. I was
not prepared to argue for I thought he had quite a strong case, so
we did some juggling with the rope in order to detach the two Sherpas and sent them back to the crevasse in charge of Kappeler. While
this was being done I looked back and noticed that a section of my
communication trench had disappeared; however, no one can have
been on it at the time or his absence would have occasioned remark.
When the rock had been cleared of snow the knife-edge presented
no difficulty and presently we were all assembled on the tip of the
gendarme thoughtfully contemplating the steep drop to the gap and
the Monk's Head still nearly a mile away. The height, I imagine, was
about 20,000 ft.

I was already convinced, and all the others agreed, that as a route
this was no go, so after an interval for photography we started for home
which we reached at 4.30 p.m. Angdawa and Ningma had come up
with more tents and wood; Ningma went back, but since we intended
going down next day Angdawa stayed to help with the loads in spite
of having no sleeping-bag. Having slept on the problem I was still of
the same mind, but Secord broached the idea that we should make
an attempt by this route without the Sherpas. His main argument was
that it was our last chance, a cogent reason but in my opinion not good
enough to justify using an unsound route. As an incident in a climb it
was very well, but it was a dangerous route over which to have to make
several journeys carrying loads. Yesterday's conditions had been ideal
but with bad weather or after fresh snow it would be unpleasant in the
extreme; moreover, the way beyond was doubtful, particularly up the
Monk's Head, and even when we were over that difficulty we were still
a very long way from the upper and easier part of the mountain. Nor
did I think we were a strong enough party to do our own load-carrying. True, on Nanda Devi we had carried our own loads, but there were
seven of us and the route was neither so difficult nor so exposed as this
one. Altogether I thought the chances of success too slim to justify the

attempt. After a long discussion we agreed to go down. It was a hard decision—especially for me. The risks were theoretical, while turning our backs on them was an irrevocable fact for which I should be largely responsible. Having had most experience I was credited—by no means of necessity rightly—with the best judgement so that my opinion would have most influence. I must play the oracle, but here no oracular vagueness or ambiguity would do. The answer must be 'yea' or 'nay' and, unlike oracles, I was involved in my own decision.

By this time it was late and once more Ningma was coughing and blowing his way up the last few steps out of the gully. He reported falling stones and the exposure of more ice as the result of avalanches and melting snow. We resolved to take only one bite at the cherry by carrying everything down with us, so every one set to work making up loads as gigantic as each thought he could cope with. Gyr and I contented ourselves with a modest 50 lb., Secord had 60 lb.; Kappeler had 80 lb. tied up like a bundle of washing in the cover of his sleeping-bag; the Sherpas in the neighbourhood of 100 lb. each, except Angtingit who took well over that. A 10 lb. tin of pemmy which no one had room for was thrown down the gully to find its own way home. In the upper part all went well, but the lower half was so icy that in one place the loads had to be lowered for 300 ft. This took time. In such places loads stick and have to be freed, bodies fail to stick and have to be stopped. See Ningma, for example, who:

> ...from the mountain top
> Pleased with the slippery surface swift descends,

and has to be stopped and fielded with some difficulty, not once but twice.

Two successive fine days had led us to believe that fine weather had set in, but that night a tempest raged, snow fell heavily, and in the morning was still falling. That, however, was no consolation for defeat, and over our 'basins of nice smooth gruel, thin, but not too thin', we faced each other pretty blankly. Gyr and I still had some hopes of the 'short-cut' to the north-west ridge, so we packed up and started for Darakush. The others remained with the intention of exploring a pass over the south-west ridge to the Dainyor nallah which in our reduced circumstances we thought should now be looked at.

Having descended as far as the foot of the moraine I discovered we had no matches, for which Angtingit, only a semi-willing victim, had to be sent back. It was raining hard at Darakush where we found a snug bivouac, tolerably free from drips, under a big boulder. Angdawa and Angtingit, who knew a thing or two, wisely slept under the boulder, generously allowing Gyr and me to spread ourselves in their spacious Logan. Like other high altitude tents, the Logan is not good in rain; but this one, a relic of Nanda Devi, was unnecessarily bad by reason of having the guys secured to the tent by a toggle inside the fabric. Where the guy passed through the fabric to the toggle, there rain passed too, so that during the night Gyr and I had to coil up smaller and smaller against the spreading flood until by morning we appeared like two small half-tide rocks.

By ten o'clock next morning the rain had let up a bit when Gyr and I started up the long scree slope, now snow-covered, leading to a wide bay at the bottom of the north-west ridge. From the upper corner of this bay it looked as though there might be a way of reaching the great snow slope which, starting from the crest of the ridge well on the summit side of Secord's knife-edge, fell steeply to within a few hundred feet of the Biro ice-fall. It was in crossing a gully below this snow slope that one of the 'corridor' reconnaissance parties had been nearly caught by an avalanche. The snow slope could not be reached from directly below and its near flank was guarded by ice-cliffs, but from the bay there seemed to be possibilities of reaching it by climbing a small tributary glacier. If this snow-slope could be reached and climbed we should land ourselves at an advanced and advantageous point on the ridge, which appeared, both to eye and camera, to be shorter and easier than the south-west spur. A harmless looking rock-step and a snow-dome seemed the worst difficulties.

After two hours' slogging we reached the mouth of the bay and sat down on a boulder for lunch. 'He that sits on a stone is twice glad.' It was not long before we got up to go whereupon Gyr found that what he rightly called his 'glare glasses' had been left behind like the Dutchman's anchor. There was in fact a remarkable absence of glare, but at these heights without glasses one can achieve snow-blindness on the dullest days, so he was forced to retire. I pushed on through very soft snow into the bay which proved to be a rock cirque cleft by several gullies. I traversed under the steep rock wall, in some places climbing the rock to avoid waist-deep patches of snow, and in time reached the upper corner where a shallow gully, almost a ledge, led to the upper part of the small tributary glacier which descends from the big snow-slope. About 500 ft. up I found a convenient but far from permanent site for a tent under a large overhanging serac, whence by cutting steps down its outside edge one could reach the glacier about twenty feet below. Since this glacier was attainable there seemed every chance of our reaching the snow-slope and finally the ridge.

After allowing a day for the snow to settle (we were still too impatient) Gyr and I went up to camp at the serac. From the very start at the mouth of the bay the route impressed itself most unfavourably upon our two Sherpas. Miniature avalanches and a few very respectable ones hissed down the several gullies from the slopes of the ridge with alarming frequency. We reached the serac without mishap and pitched the tent. The two Sherpas started down and we heard later that Angtingit had come unstuck on the shelf and had finished up well out in the middle of the bay, for which unlucky incident our route received (in this case unjustly) another black mark. Before pitching the tent I had cut down to the glacier with the intention of camping higher, but as the glacier surface was bare ice which would involve more step-cutting we decided to content ourselves where we were. In the evening, which was fine, we improved the steps and Gyr reconnoitred a way out from our gîte by the rock-wall above the shelf.

In the morning we woke to find a foot of snow and a thick mist. There was nothing for it but to go down. By this time the others had arrived and they, too, had had adventures. They had climbed to the top of the col on the south-west ridge and were confident that we could descend the other side, but the Matun Das col which they had also tried had foiled them by a rope's length. They had pressed the attack until dark and until Kappeler, who was leading, had come off and nearly demolished the expectant Secord.

On 2 July Gyr and I tried again. Our two Sherpas had the air of unwilling martyrs in a not very worthy cause, and I must say they had good reason for their dejection. Before we reached the bay the debris of a large avalanche slid gently to rest at our feet, while in the bay still others fell before and behind us with even more distressing frequency than before. There was at least one of some weight which roared down from another gully right at the foot of our own. In order to camp in a safer place and to avoid the short icy descent to the glacier we tried to break out of our shallow gully by the rock-wall on our left. It was too steep and the Sherpas refused, so we went on to the serac where Gyr repeated his climb of the wall to see if we could haul up the loads and the Sherpas. It was no good, and in the end we both had to 'abseil' down a short icy funnel to the ice-cave under the serac. The Sherpas, having watched these manoeuvres with concern, then departed.

Next morning when Gyr and I dropped down on to the little tributary glacier by the steps already cut we were blessed with a fine day, just as we had been on the one critical day on the south-west spur. Although the snow had peeled off, leaving the glacier bare, the slope was so gradual that we mounted rapidly, having only to nick a few steps. Wishing to get off the ice on to snow we left the glacier and steered a course for some cliffs. Under these there was plenty of snow of a kind soft enough and deep enough for a water buffalo to wallow in. In order to climb out of this morass Gyr led directly up the cliff and after steep climbing gained footing on a rock and snow-rib. The little glacier was now far below and the big snow-slope less readily attainable, for the ice-cliffs guarding it ran up unbroken to meet our rib some 2000 ft. above. Like boxers side-stepping to avoid trouble we had overdone it and stepped right out of the ring. It takes a strong mind to throw away height laboriously gained, so instead of descending to the glacier and a sure route we trusted ourselves to luck and the rib. For the rib itself beckoned us invitingly upwards and beyond its junction with the ice-cliff a snow-scoop led directly to the ridge.

The climb which followed was arduous and at times, I thought, perilous. Having followed our rib to the bitter end, I eventually found myself with one shoulder wedged against the ice-cliff, which was about thirty feet high, grubbing away in soft snow lying on ice in an endeavour to reach the scoop beyond. Owing to the underlying ice neither of us was secure. We started to discuss retreat, in fact we had already begun to move down, when looking back we noticed a rock island sticking out of the ice not far from the foot of the ice-cliff. To go down now would waste the whole day so we determined to try it. The passage

Monk's Head *en face* from below south-west spur

Monk's Head in profile from north-west ridge

View from camp on spur looking over south-west ridge
to Haramosh on left and Dobani on right

across the bare ice was awkward, but Gyr reached the rock safely and led on up to the foot of the scoop. Here the snow became thinner and thinner. Below lay hard blue ice and to break out of the scoop on to the snow slope, or to follow it to the top, would entail long and arduous step-cutting. Having already said so much about eyes, cameras, and their ideas of angles, I will not attempt to estimate the angle of the slope out of the scoop, but it was of daunting steepness. We went down 200 or 300 ft., found a break in the ice-cliff which we had overlooked, gained the big snow-slope, and at two o'clock sat down for lunch a hundred feet below the crest of the ridge, wondering why we had not seen the break before.

Having eaten we dragged ourselves to the ridge for by now we were both pretty tired. We thought the ridge at this point was something over 20,000 ft. The 'serac' camp we estimated to be 15,000ft. and having left it at 6 a.m. we had been climbing steadily and steeply for seven hours. Our situation was very grand. Over the curling cornices of the south-west spur we looked to the ice-fluted ridge beyond, and over that far away to the white flashing pyramid of Haramosh (24,270 ft.) and the massive Dobani (20,126 ft.). On the north side the Hunza valley lay spread at our feet, or rather 13,000 ft. below them, so far below that fields, villages, and barren earth blended into one brown smudge. But of more moment was the view eastwards along the ridge. A quarter of a mile away, what had seemed from below to be but a harmless rock-step now took shape as a formidable gendarme. We were too tired to visit it, but we were close enough to see that for porters it would be a serious obstacle; if our minds needed making up, this new trouble was decisive, although I think we had already tacitly decided that this route, too, was no go. Try as one might there was no ignoring the fact that at the start the avalanche danger was considerable, and though our difficult line of ascent would not be repeated the alternative line up the snow-slope was not a route by which we could with clear consciences bring up porters. That evening we descended it direct and found it devilish steep, the snow uncertain, and in places ready to avalanche.

We reached the tent at 6 p.m. to be greeted by a brisk discharge of snow cataracts into the cirque and by the strident roar of a more formidable avalanche from the same offending gully hard by. We packed up, listening uneasily to these monitory voices, whose message for us seemed to be that of a familiar hymn:

> Lo, it is not yours to say
> When to march and when to rest.

We waited till dark, for that night there was a full moon. Unluckily it chose to rise immediately behind Rakaposhi and so far as we were concerned it need not have troubled to rise at all. As another hymn goes, 'the night is black, the feet are slack', but we stumbled down in safety, carrying all the gear, and were met by the Sherpas with lights half-way down the long scree slope. And so to Darakush to meet our companions and to extinguish their last hope.

CHAPTER VII

THE DAINYOR NALLAH

◆

As Gyr and I wolfed a late supper we all sat by a big fire discussing plans. Since it is a poor plan which admits no modifications, ours on the whole must have been good, for they were repeatedly frustrated and had to be just as repeatedly revised. Though Secord and Kappeler were disappointed by our gloomy report they were hardly surprised, for Angdawa's account of the 'via dolorosa' to the 'serac' camp had lost nothing in the telling. The possibilities of the Jaglot nallah having been exhausted, the next best thing seemed to be a descent into the Dainyor nallah by the new pass to see if there was any possible route there. Not that we should be certain to attempt the mountain again if there was, for it was now 4 July, a week would be needed to take the stores round, and Secord and I were due to leave by the end of the month. Were we to discover a very promising route, then a struggle between duty and pleasure might occur.

While waiting for coolies from Jaglot to bring the stores down from the Kunti camp we had a day of rest. It was very hot and cloudless. Secord's friends the flies were out in full force in spite of the fact that the cows had long since left. For the future I made a resolve not to begin climbing until assured by a plague of flies that summer had really come.

On the 5th we walked up the Manogar with two Sherpas and camped by the last of the wood. The col we were to cross was reported to be 'not very easy', so we sent the Sherpas back and went on ourselves carrying three days' food. We took no tents except for a very light one of Secord's weighing 6 lb. Having crossed the foot of the Kunti glacier we climbed a wide snow-fan which gradually narrowed to a couloir. A hundred feet or so below the short rock-pitch which led to the summit of the col our leader became involved in some step-cutting. Until then we had been comfortably kicking our way up in good hard snow. This unwelcome change of tactics gave rise to a warm argument between two schools of thought—the rock limpets and the snow hogs—as to whether, since the ice appeared to continue to the foot of the rock-pitch, it would not be better to take to the rock-wall of the couloir at once. The point at issue was settled by Gyr, who, taking a giant stride into the centre of the narrow couloir, triumphantly thrust his axe into snow and began kicking a large step; much in the same way that Johnson refuted Bishop Berkeley's proof of the non-existence of matter by kicking with mighty force a large stone, exclaiming with equal force: 'I refute it thus.' Whereupon Kappeler and I on the second rope ungraciously moved up past them, leaving the rock limpet to detach himself as best he could from the rocks to which he was already clinging.

The short rock-pitch to the top was very enjoyable. It was not difficult and the rock was of sound granite, a regrettably rare occurence in the Himalaya. We had been climbing for four hours and we put the height at 15,000 ft. It might well have been 16,000 ft. but our candid friends the altimeters refused to believe that it was a foot more than 14,000 ft. On the other side of the col (or pass as we were now entitled to call it) only a few feet away, the rock reverted to the Himalayan average of rottenness. Like burglars descending a creaking staircase, we picked our way down a treacherous little gully to emerge presently on a snow-field where we had lunch. It was not easy to decide whether the snow-field was the remnant of a glacier or the embryo of one, but it did not extend far and soon we began plunging down boulders, scree, and finally grass, to fetch up at a little alp and a hut situated on a shelf above the Dainyor glacier. Opposite to us on the other side of the glacier was another col. This we took to be Conway's Uchubagan col which he had climbed from the Bagrot nallah and which had given him his glimpse of Rakaposhi.

The south ridge of Rakaposhi on which this col lies was clearly of no use to us, for between the col and the mountain lay a high and difficult peak. At the head of the Dainyor glacier, between the south and south-west ridges, was a very long, steep, and dangerous looking snow-slope, while coming down from the south-west ridge was a reentrant into which we could not properly see. But we knew what that ridge was like, so we soon came to the conclusion that there was nothing here for us.

We followed a path leading down the valley and presently, a few miles down, we found ourselves in delightful needle-carpeted pine forest. As I was steaming along in front looking for fresh water by which to camp I heard an agonized cry, or possibly a Swiss oath, from behind. Gyr had slipped and sprained an ankle—an accident to which even mountaineers are not immune if careless, tired, or in a devil of a hurry. Thus, our camp site was determined, and it happened not to be a bad one, under a friendly canopy of pines with just enough water for our needs. It was good to have found an eligible camp, but more important was whether we should be able to leave it, for Gyr's ankle had by now puffed up to an alarming size. After some tea I walked on down the path to see where we had got to. Half a mile on the forest petered out at the tip of an ancient moraine strewn with boulders. Here there was a clear view down the valley, and here, picking a sparse living from between the boulders, was a herd of goats tended by two men. One was dumb and the other half-witted, but both successfully 'registered' what I took to be astonishment. Very frequently one finds that the village goats are herded by a man with some such affliction, and I often wonder whether it is that which marks them out for the office or whether the affliction is the result of their long communion with goats. Rational conversation with a dumb man or a half-wit is at all times difficult, but more so when there is no common language. But my dumb friend seemed very much 'all there' and I gathered from him that there was a short way back to Matun Das up a big nallah which I could see coming in from the north two or three miles down.

The weather considerately allowed us a good night's sleep and time to start the fire before heavy rain set in to quench it. Painful though Gyr's ankle must have been, it was a great relief to find that he could get a boot on and hobble. Below the old moraine were many abandoned fields and presently we came to the first dwelling where we got a lot of milk but very little information; while at the first village a mile or so on the people were very off-hand indeed, and would give us neither one nor the other. This village was situated at the junction of the nallah I had seen the day before and the Dainyor. To follow the Dainyor stream down to the main valley below Gilgit and then back up to Jaglot would be a long way, and we had already vaguely learnt that there was a short-cut to Matun Das, the village below Jaglot close by the rope bridge.

If a short-cut existed it must lie up this nallah, but the head of it was out of sight and we knew from the map and the lie of the land that to reach Matun Das that way we should have to cross some very high ground indeed. From this village we could see another path which struck straight up the hillside, evidently heading for the Hunza valley somewhere on the other side but not in the direction of Matun Das. Should we play for safety by taking this, or be bold and with only one day's food left go up the unseen nallah and trust to luck? Secord was not in favour of either. 'No matter where it lead me, the downward path for me', was his view as he pointed down the Dainyor. Questions of food and funk decided it, as they often do, and in the midday heat we began the plod up bare, waterless, seemingly interminable slopes. Having gained some height we could see at the head of the nallah a deep notch of rock and snow and above it a nice looking peak of some 19,000 ft. The notch looked crossable, but to cross it would have meant another day and a hungry one.

Having had a dry lunch under a tree which had a sad, drooping air, as if it had taken root there one day inadvertently and regretted it ever since, we at last reached a saddle on the ridge some 3000 ft. above the village. On the other side was a wide nallah which would obviously take us in quick time to Jutal (the village below Matun Das), and to water as well, from the lack of which we were all beginning to feel a bit peevish. Secord, having fallen in once with our whims and having sweated for it, was resolved not to do so again. Like a thirst-maddened horse scenting water from afar, he shot down the 'khud' in a cloud of dust and small stones. We other three were in a pig-headed mood. Having gained 3000 ft. of height at the cost of a prodigious thirst we were bent on making some use of it, regardless of the fact that sooner or later we should have to drop to the main valley. But we scorned to 'bummel' along it and if there was no short-cut direct to Matun Das, then we would make one. The fact that the track we had followed so far continued in the direction of the fast disappearing Secord counted for nothing, for a faint broken scar along the bare stony hillside at our level suggested that in Buddhist times or some earlier era there had been a high-level route to Matun Das.

Secord, rightly suspecting that our need might be greater than his, had generously left us the bulk of the remaining food, so that Gyr in spite of his damaged ankle was not unwilling to cast in his lot with the high-level party. Off we went through brambles, briars, boulders, casting about for traces of a path and more anxiously for signs of water. There was not a hint of this, but we came upon some fine thick rhubarb. Some was sucked on the spot and some taken for supper. By four o'clock we had reached a rock-shoulder where the tenuous path ended for good. Ahead was a deep nallah and we strained our ears vainly listening for the sound of water. High above some snow-beds still lingered on—there must be water somewhere—so off we went again on a high traverse only to become spread-eagled on some cliffs. Secord, we reflected, must by now have finished his last cup of tea and would be reaching for his pipe. Hunger makes men bold, thirst makes them foolhardy. Recklessly we plunged down a horrible loose gully—Gyr twisting his ankle once more in his haste—by means of which, just before dark, we reached the nallah bed, water, and some old withered junipers.

It was a queer place for a camp. To sleep we had to hollow out coffin-like scoops in the loose rock, to fetch wood we had to climb up, and to draw water we had to climb down. Only immediately opposite our bivouac was there any way out on the opposing side. Upstream and down the rock-walls leant over the narrow bed where the water dashed unquietly from rock to rock and from one cascade to another. Lying on our stone shelves at the bottom of this stone crevasse we looked up to a ribbon of steel-blue sky across which the stars sailed slowly like lights on a dark river.

At dawn we woke to a clap of thunder. Hastily blowing up the fire we turned the remnant of our flour into chapattis and as the storm broke we ate them as we crouched under the overhanging wall of the gorge. When the rain was over we crossed the river and climbed out of this friendly nallah to continue traversing over rocky slopes which appeared to have been ploughed by some giant hand into ridge and furrow. At ten o'clock we came to a grass shoulder beyond which was a deep valley and a path. We had had our bellyful of traversing this trackless hillside. Obstinate pride gave way to sweet reasonableness and we took the path which must lead, as we well knew, only to Jutal.

Having so far refused to yield an inch of the height we had gained so laboriously yesterday we had now about 7000 ft. to descend pretty abruptly, but we found some scree-slopes which allowed us to make such short work of this long plunge into the Hunza valley that we arrived at Jutal by midday. We retain kindly memories of Jutal where the villagers fed the chastened wanderers on eggs and delicious bread which tasted like well-leavened bannocks. Later in the day the lambardar conducted us to the outskirts of his village, past the inevitable polo ground, and there dismissed us to follow the track by the left bank of the river to Matun Das and Jaglot. Early in the march we encountered two characteristic features of this country—a blinding sandstorm whipped up from the sand-banks of the river, and a fine example of a 'parri', a well-known word here indicating a precipice across which the path is taken. Sometimes it is made by hewing out the rock, sometimes by supporting the path on a stone revetment, and sometimes, in extreme cases, by supporting it on wooden brackets driven into the wall of the precipice which may be either of rock or boulder-clay. On this particular' parri' the path is dangerously narrow so that transport animals cannot use it.

Instead of climbing up to Matun Das, which lies on a shelf 200 or 300 ft. above the river, we slunk past below in the extravagant hope that Secord, whom we suspected would be there gorging fruit, might believe we had reached Jaglot by an even shorter cut than we had hoped. This over-careful regard for saving face cost us the rest and refreshment we might have had. By seven o'clock we were at the foot of the steep climb out of the main valley and we gained the open fields above in time to see Rakaposhi aglow with the rays of a sun which for us had already set. The north-west ridge looked to be an easy walk, while the Monk's Head, I thought, leered at us scornfully. The Sherpas were there with all our stores and, having eaten an omelette of Himalayan grandeur prepared by Angdawa, we lay down to sleep under the apricots.

After a morning's haggling we settled our account for coolies, mutton, and milk, and started for Matun Das, bathing on the way in a 'kul'. These main 'kuls' are two or three feet deep, several feet wide, and sometimes several miles long. There is a famous one—the Berber—at Baltit, the capital of Hunza, which is six miles long. Once a year they are cleaned out and the fine alluvial deposit is used to enrich the fields.

Matun Das, outside the borders of Hunza proper, is a Hunza colony, as the well-terraced fields, the orchards, and the well-kept 'kuls' bear witness. We found Secord there in company with our friend Mainprice who was on his way to Jaglot to strike the first blow in the construction of his new 'kul', the opposition of the Jaglot elders having at last been overcome. They were reclining more or less gracefully in an orchard surrounded by trays of peaches, figs, apricots, and apples, both looking, I thought, understandably pale. Small boys reappeared frequently with more trays and baskets, received their few annas, and departed for fresh supplies. In the end these imports had to be summarily stopped, more in the interests of our stomachs than our pockets.

Once more we were faced with the necessity of making a plan, and I began to have a sneaking admiration for our professional planners who make such things with less trouble than we should take to strike a match. It was now 10 July, we had about a fortnight left, and our first thought was to visit the Bagrot nallah to round off the reconnaissance of the mountain which we had failed to climb. One objection to this was that if we went the shortest way by the left bank of the Hunza river we should pass within a stone's throw of Gilgit on the opposite bank. This we thought would be carrying austerity too far and might even be considered discourteous to the residents. A graver objection was that if we should discover later that we ought to have gone there in the first place rather than to Jaglot, then our consequent regret and remorse would be too poignant to bear. Moreover, the Bagrot nallah was not new ground and ever since our first glance at our map (Survey of India, ¼ in., Sheet 42L) we had been tantalized by the presence of a long white strip of glacier marked 'unexplored'. About half this map-sheet is unsurveyed, the dividing line being roughly the Batura-Muztagh range which runs in a northwesterly direction from Baltit until it meets the Hindu Kush on the Hunza-Wakhan border. The triangular tract north of this range, between it and the Hindu Kush and west of the Hunza river, had been surveyed pretty thoroughly by the Dutch Visser-Hooft expedition of 1925 and the Montagnier expedition of 1927, both of which had had the assistance of Indian surveyors lent by the Survey of India. South of the range, as far as the Gilgit river, the country is not only unsurveyed but is in a few places still unexplored, so that the map is for the most part more or less intelligent guess-work.

Whether an unexplored portion should be left a clean white blank on the map or whether it should be drawn in, in speculative fashion, fitting as best it may into the contiguous surveyed area is a nice point. Like a great many of us, some explorers wish to have their cake and eat it. They enjoy the thrill and claim the credit of traversing new country and at the same time are ungrateful enough to complain of the inadequacy of the map. The genuine explorer would prefer, I think, to have with him a Snark-hunter's map—a complete and absolute blank—upon which he could first exercise his own talent for intelligent guess-work and then later by experience discover his own mistakes. On the part of the map in question the guessing had already been done for us and its results, merely by being published, had acquired a sufficently authoritative air to induce us, foolishly perhaps, to base our plan upon them. On any but the most modern maps of mountainous country—and in the Himalaya there are now many such, thanks to the Survey of India and private exploration—one expects the detail to be wrong or vague, but takes for granted that the general lie of the land is as represented.

Referring to the map it will be seen that the Bola Das river, entering the Hunza river near Chalt from the north, has its origin in two big glaciers near a place called Toltar. The eastern branch, the Baltar, we found had been visited by Col. R. F. C. Schomberg who had also seen the first few miles of the larger northern branch, but no one had been to the head of this, which, according to the draughtsman, extended for more than fifteen miles between the Batura-Muztagh range on the east and another rather queer-looking range to the west. West again of this was the Karumbar river and reality. Though it did not, it should have occurred to us at the time that there really was not much room for a glacier of this size and another mountain range between the Batura-Muztagh range and the Karumbar valley. Anyhow we accepted the draughtsman's dream, guess, or fancy at its face value and laid our plans accordingly. Having allowed ourselves seven days to reach the northern end of the unexplored glacier, perhaps climbing an easy peak on the way, we should cross a pass (which we should no doubt find) leading either to the Koz Yaz or Yashkuk Yaz glaciers. We preferred the former but we would not be too particular. Both these glaciers we knew to be as drawn on the map, for they had been surveyed by the Visser-Hooft party. But if by some mischance there was no pass to

The north-west ridge with point on it reached by Gyr and Tilman
marked ×; the big snow slope lies to the right of the route line.
Monk's Head on right edge of picture

Lower part of north-west ridge from Darakush.
Peak climbed by Secord and Vivyan 1938 on left.
× = point reached by Gyr and Tilman. Rock cirque
and snow bay about centre of picture

Looking across Kunti glacier to Dainyor pass

either, then we should have to break out over the western wall to the
Karumbar valley. That was all right so far as it went; but we were no
dithering amateurs planning a Sunday School treat for one afternoon.
We were engaged in long-term planning, according to the best modern
practice, and so having crossed the pass, say, to the Koz Yaz glacier,
the party would then crack a bottle of 'Ovosport', shake hands, and
disintegrate. Secord would bend his weary steps westwards to Chitral
via the Chillinji pass and many others which were no concern of ours;
I, having accompanied the Swiss down the Chapursan valley as far as
Misgar, would head happily northwards, once more free from care; and
the Swiss would turn southwards from Misgar, pay their respects to
the Mirs of Hunza and Nagar, and continue with whatever they might
have a mind to. But as the Spanish proverb has it: 'He that shuffles
does not always cut.'

Since Secord had first to have permission to go out through Chitral and since I had some things to collect for my Kashgar trip, we were
obliged to return to Gilgit before setting forth on this new venture. The
thought of having to do twice more the seventeen miles between Nomal
and Gilgit was sufficient to modify any transports of joy we might have
felt at the prospect of a few days in Gilgit with our friends. We had not
been out long enough or fared hard enough to have any overpowering
longing for the flesh-pots, but on the other hand it would be churlish
to refuse the hospitality that would certainly be offered. 'When they
bring you the heifer be ready with the rope', were the words of advice
most frequently uttered by Sancho Panza.

We recrossed the bridge to Nomal, Angdawa once more having to
be carried, and left there again at noon on a blistering hot day. We had
already sent off a courier to announce our coming and at Nomal we
mounted Kappeler, who had a stiff knee, on a 'Rosinante' of a pony,
and sent him off as a second herald, having some doubt about the
energy or willingness of the first. We advised Kappeler to spare neither
man nor beast; but although the foot party started some time later we
soon caught him up and in the end arrived in Gilgit dirty, hot, shaggy,
and unannounced.

CHAPTER VIII

THE KUKUAY GLACIER

CHALT, OUR STARTING-POINT, is the next stage beyond Nomal. The distance is only fifteen miles, but for many of these the track lies over sand or loose pebbles. On either hand are bare rock-walls and once the sun tops these the traveller has no relief from its concentrated power until he reaches Chalt. Good judges of misery, amateurs with a taste for suffering, would hardly know to which stage to award the palm—Gilgit to Nomal or Nomal to Chalt. This straggling village occupies the alluvial fans deposited by the Chaprot and Bola Das nallahs and its fort once commanded the routes of Hunza and Nagar. Thus Chalt and its fort became at one time a bone of contention between the petty states of Hunza and Nagar as well as between these states and the Kashmir garrison at Gilgit. In 1891 when British authority had to be asserted over the Mirs of Hunza and Nagar because of their defiant attitude towards the British Agent, Chalt was the advanced base for the troops whose formidable task was to storm the strong position of Nilt a few miles up stream on the opposite bank.

As usual the bungalow was at the farthest and highest point of the fan. We arrived at midday in a gale of wind to find awaiting us the 'thesildar' from Gilgit whom Col. Bacon had kindly sent to help us in our negotiations for coolies. In addition to this Col. Bacon had advised the Mir of Hunza that we should shortly be coming down the Chapursan valley, which is in his territory, and had asked him to send someone up there to assure the people that the coming invaders were neither Afghan nor Russian. Presently the local rajah arrived with a gift of fruit. We arranged transport rates with him and then we settled down to serious business with the lambardar. The lambardar of a village is the man who makes or mars the getting of coolies or ponies, while the chowkidar is equally powerful in the matter of food and quarters. I never quite got the hang of local government. I suppose there was in reality only one 'King of Brentford', but when it came to distributing largesse we found there were seldom less than five lambardars and more than one chowkidar.

The lambardar of Chalt, a spare, oldish, dignified man was much-travelled, having made the journey to Kashgar several times. Wishing to enlarge the bounds of his experience he made us the welcome offer of his company, but that evening he and the thesildar had a slight tiff during which I feared we should lose the services of this valuable ally and that the ally himself would lose his life. It seemed that ponies could only be used for the first seven miles up the Bola Das whence we should need ten coolies to carry for us up the glacier. Some sample 60 lb. loads had been made up, around which there gathered an interested circle of idlers, critics, and prospective carriers all eyeing the loads rather lugubriously. The lambardar agreed with them that 60 lb. was too much; the thesildar, acting for us, thought otherwise. A weight-lifting contest began, one party handling the loads as a professional on the stage handles a 200 lb. lift, the veins starting out on their foreheads as they grunted and heaved, while our party, represented by the Sherpas, flipped them about contemptuously like men stacking bricks. We seemed to be getting nowhere, until the thesildar, his rage suddenly kindling, clutched with both hands a 60 lb. bag of atta and hurled it violently at the semi-venerable lambardar, sending him reeling to the ground. Since the lambardar was not killed and since soon after he was even able to stand, everyone agreed that 60 lb. had been proved by demonstration to be a very fair load.

Two or three miles up the Bola Das nallah is the village of Budelas. We were standing in a field buying flour, idly viewing the sullen clouds to the east, when suddenly above the cloud a small white triangle, faint but harder than a cloud, took shape—it was the summit of Rakaposhi. The clouds began slowly to dissolve upon the face of the superb pyramid and its plinth of ice, the north-west ridge rose above them like a white whale breaking surface, and the grandest view of the mountain we had yet seen burst upon us—one from which it was hard to turn away. The north-west ridge was to us three-quarters on; we should have preferred it square on so that Secord's peak, the knife-edge section, the point reached by Gyr and me, and the gendarme beyond, could have been identified more easily. A few miles on we came to some hot springs, where the coolies took over the loads and our forceful friend the thesildar bade us farewell. His semi-venerable victim, armed with a mighty staff, now took his place as guide and counsellor.

Water from the hot spring having been led into a rough stone tank and the plug, in the form of clods of earth, having been inserted, the bath filled itself and the distinguished visitors bathed. We then moved on up the narrowing valley, crossed the Daintar nallah, and finished the march to Bar with a delightfully easy and pleasant walk alongside a 'kul' several hundred feet above the river. The people of Bar seemed marvellously ill-favoured, but were eager to see us and ready to supply us. I was amused and sorry to see the precaution taken by a little old man who guided us through the village, running ahead to warn any approaching women of the invasion of infidel males. Those who were about at once scurried off the track to hide in the crops, or else pulled a 'lungi' over their face. If women are more curious than men, which I doubt, then Moslem women must suffer agonies from its enforced repression. Think of what a sight they had to deny themselves now, one which would not (though it did) pass that way again. An uncommonly long European, a short young European gentleman, a black-bearded professor-like European, a grizzled veteran, and four strange smooth-faced, slit-eyed, coloured gentlemen.

At Bar some shuffling of our coolie team took place, some Chalt men went back while Bar men took their places. Two recruits also joined us here—Robinson Crusoe and Man Friday—who said they had been some way up our glacier after ibex and proposed now to show us the way and to keep us in meat. Crusoe was the embodiment of unquenchable optimism, as indeed he had to be to hunt ibex with his primitive firelock—a long gas-pipe innocent of sights with a couple of wooden prongs like the business-end of a hay-fork mounted on the barrel as a rest. The firing mechanism was a length of fuse wound round the butt, its lighted end held poised above the pan by a clip; on pressing the trigger this descended with decorum on to the primed pan and in due course a large round bullet proceeded up the barrel to speed gravely on its deadly mission. Man Friday carried this weighty antiquity, Crusoe the accessories, which were slung round his person in little skin bags—powder, balls, flint and steel, tinder, wadding, and ramrod.

Four miles beyond Bar is another small hamlet—the last outpost of civilization—above which, on the old terminal moraine of the glacier, the track becomes sketchy and the going bad in the extreme. We reached the junction of the two glaciers at one o'clock. The eastern branch which originates under two 25,000 ft. peaks on the Batura-Muztagh range was called by the locals Baltar, while our unexplored glacier, which from here bore away slightly north of west, was known as the Kukuay. That day's destination was the sheepfold of Burjukush three miles away on the south side of the glacier, but owing to the rough going and the consequent slowness of the coolies it was always doubtful as to whether we should make it. However, the promise of a sheep persuaded them at least to try. Just short of Burjukush a glacier stream, the Aldarkush, comes in from the south. When we reached it in late evening it was in full spate, but Crusoe, our guide, having climbed a hill and gazed long at the turbulent flood, beckoned us on. There was no sign of a bridge, but presently Crusoe began stripping his nether garments and we realised the bridge was of a peculiar kind—an Irish bridge—for most of the water was going over it instead of under. Here both Crusoe and Man Friday worked their passage by standing for minutes at a time in the icy torrent helping Sherpas and coolies across and sometimes carrying their loads. The shepherds and their charges were in residence. After due haggling two sheep were slaughtered and everyone turned in happy, except perhaps myself who in the role of Moses overheard the murmuring of his people at the length of their first march into the wilderness and their avowed intention of making the next very short.

From the old moraine bank between alp and glacier we could see that two miles up another glacier (the Sat Marau, or Seven Ibex—which a shikari had once killed there) swept down from the west in a wild jumble of ice, and that beyond this the Kukuay took a more promising northerly course. Around the bend, and still on our side, there was a fine birch spinney, probably the last, the obvious place for our next camp, provided the thoughts of camel and camel-drivers would agree. We made a late start at eight o'clock and the pace set, which was not even a brisk crawl, suggested that so far at least these thoughts were totally at variance. No effort was made to take the decisive step down to the glacier; instead we shunned it as though it were a quicksand, creeping through the jungle of trees and bushes growing in the ablation valley behind the old moraine, until it became clear that no such drastic step was in view but that the intention was to camp on the moraine well short of the bend. Having first won over to our point of view the lambardar and Crusoe we called a conference of coolies and persuaded them by a mixture of imprecation and cajolery to commit themselves to the glacier. Once we were there, the elements came to our help, for it began to drizzle and since there were huts at the spinney everyone got a move on.

We were now out in the middle of an ice-sea, or more correctly a sea of stones, for the Kukuay bears down on its surface great quantities of stone and debris deposited by either the numerous tributary glaciers from the west or by the mighty cliffs of the Batura peaks on the east. An exceedingly rough sea it was—a maze of waves and troughs. At one place where a mass of white marble debris lay, the waves seemed to be breaking in foam on some reef. For five hours we threaded our way in and out of the hollows of this tumbled surface, for there was neither lateral nor medial moraine, nor any grassy ablation valley to ease our progress. Having landed at last on the western shore we climbed steeply to our camp among the birches, a place whose name we were told was also Darakush. The trees surrounded a clear unrippled tarn in whose water the reflected peaks vied in beauty with the peaks themselves.

Astonishment is a salutary emotion and the Kukuay glacier administered it to us in large doses. From the snout its course had been a little north of west, it had then swung to the north, and now it appeared to be coming from a point well to the east of north. The draughtsman's dream which had been committed to paper now became for us a nightmare where we talked of nothing but courses steered and distance run in order to arrive at some sort of dead reckoning. One thing was clear— that we were a long way from the Koz Yaz glacier, and that to bring us within striking distance of it the Kukuay glacier would have to mend its ways and behave as the draughtsman had expected.

Crusoe and Friday were now bidden to bestir themselves and fulfil their office. They therefore arranged a crack-of-dawn start for themselves in order to catch the ibex asleep, for this, I should say, was the only way by which they could get within killing distance. They would then meet us (bringing home the bacon, we hoped) at another alp called Little Darakush. This was four miles up on the far side of another

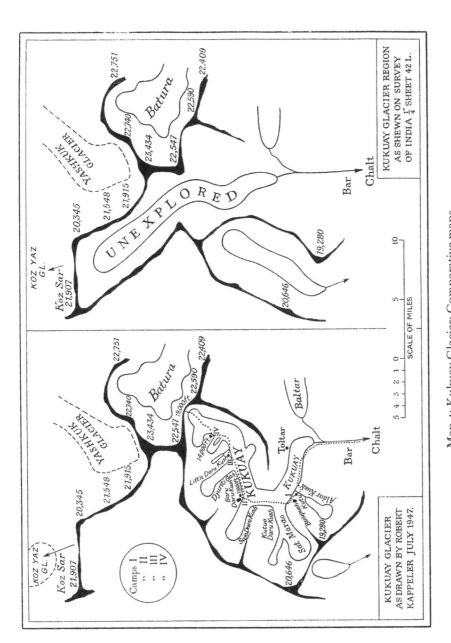

Map 4: Kukuay Glacier: Comparative maps

big tributary glacier and it was the bourne beyond which no traveller had yet gone. There would be grass but no birch trees. We reached it in two hours of glacier-walking over a rather better surface. It proved to be a very pleasant grass flat tucked in between the old moraine and some cliffs, the home of choughs and ravens. Dwarf willow, whose dead branches made excellent firewood, grew profusely on the moraine, while under the cliff wild rhubarb flourished as though in a hot-bed; blue and yellow violets and golden columbine graced the sward, but the only water in this alpine garden was that obtained from a snow-bed which still lingered in the cool shadow of the cliff. The height, we thought, was 12,500 ft.

As we approached this place we had noticed away up on our left an easy-looking snow col of moderate height at the upper end of this big tributary glacier which the locals called Djuriti Gah. We had made a careful note of this as a possible way of escape to the Karumbar in case the Kukuay played us false as seemed now not unlikely. After lunch we climbed to a vantage point and saw not far ahead a long stretch of dry clean ice which promised fast easy travelling, while beyond the glacier curled round a high rock cape on a more northerly course. This raised our hopes. We had now covered about twelve miles up the glacier and had it followed more or less the expected course we should now have been within a few miles of its termination and the divide between it and the Chapursan glacier system. Instead of this it had described almost a semicircle and the dry debris-free ice seemed to indicate that the end was not far off, but that end could not be where we hoped.

Spurred on by curiosity we dropped down to glacier level, found an intricate way on to it by a corridor of black, dirty ice, reached the clean, smooth surface beyond, and went on at our best speed. After about a mile and a half we reached and rounded the cape, but there the greater part of our hopes died. Four or five miles away a great snow cirque marked, without room for mistake, the beginning and for us the end of the Kukuay. Far up in the high north-east corner of the cirque a dwindling arm of the glacier curved out of sight and our prospects of crossing the cirque seemed to depend on what there was round the corner. If there was a col it must be high, the approach by an ice-fall looked difficult, and what lay beyond was anybody's guess. Most of us thought that the answer would prove to be the Yashkuk glacier, but we had an uneasy feeling that it might just as well be the Batura, for we had already identified (or so we thought) the big 23,434 ft. peak on the main Batura range. Subdued and sorrowful we walked back to camp where our sorrows were slightly alleviated by a gigantic rhubarb pie of Angdawa's baking.

Having dumped one load of atta in favour of a load of firewood, for our journey up the glacier had taken less than the estimated time, we started on our last march with the men of Chalt and Bar. It was a hot cloudless day, indeed the weather so far had been so good that we doubted our wisdom in leaving Rakaposhi. Below the rock-cape was a meagre supply of wood, but as we were anxious to get the most out of the coolies while we had them we pushed on for another half-hour and finally pitched our camp on the last rocks.

We paid off the coolies and tipped the lambardar, Crusoe, and Man Friday. Tipping is always difficult and the thought of having given too little is almost as hard to bear as the thought of having given too much. This time it was more difficult than usual because the coolies had earned more than what I proposed giving to their elders and betters, for neither the lambardar nor the two shikaris had carried any loads. However, we shook hands and parted amicably enough, little thinking that we should see each other again—one reason, perhaps, why I felt that the tipping need not be overdone. One stout-hearted man of Bar decided to stay with us to see the outcome. He had proposed this hazardous course at the start, but I had not paid much attention, thinking that his complete inability to converse either with ourselves or the Sherpas, the roughness of glacier travel, and the sight of large quantities of ice and snow at the end of it would have cooled his ardour when the time came. The rigour and loneliness of his future life were kindly pointed out, but his determination was unshaken. So we fitted him out with what spare things we had and took him on—and well worth while he proved.

From our camp (c. 14,000 ft.) we estimated we should have to climb about 5000 ft. to reach the snow cirque. Even from here the col, if any, was out of sight, but the approach by the ice-fall did not look so difficult as it had done from lower down. Next morning, the 21st, we four started at the first faint hint of daylight. We made good time up the dry ice of the glacier, but even so it took us over two hours to reach the foot of the ice-fall. At this early hour the snow was so hard that in places steps had to be cut, but it enabled us to cross with confidence two frail snow bridges over wide and deep crevasses. We could now see the col at the far end of a wide and flat snow corridor. From underneath it did not appear inviting so we discarded it in favour of one slightly higher on the north side of the corridor which here ran almost east and west. Having crossed a bergschrund at the foot we began climbing a long snow-slope of about 60° where only the last 200 ft., where the snow lay thinly on ice, gave any trouble. The consummation of a week's travel was upon us. As we scrambled up the summit rocks to decide the issue, hope and doubt were equally balanced.

What we saw on the other side was satisfactory only because of its decisiveness. Sometimes on reaching a col which one hopes to cross the worst is not revealed until one is more than half-way down, when the dislike of going back is only matched by the dislike of going on. But here an impossibly steep drop at our feet left us in no doubt at all, so that the prudent had not to incur the suspicion of timidity by objecting to a route which the boldest dared not commend. Had there been a chance of going down, the fact that the glacier so far below was undoubtedly the Batura might have dissuaded us from the attempt, though to travel in the wrong direction is probably preferable to retracing one's steps. It was now clear that we were not north of the big 23,434 ft. peak as we had thought, but were probably between the two 22,000 ft. peaks to the south of it and barely ten miles north of the junction of the Kukuay and Baltar glaciers. Glaciers are sometimes as erratic as men, and only when both behave in a normal way do they become dull. I was never more disappointed in my life than by the perfectly normal behaviour of the 'Cornice' glacier, near the junction of the Hispar and Biafo glaciers, of which the account of earlier explorers[*] (whom I dearly wished to believe) had led me to hope that it was unique among glaciers in that it had no outlet, being entirely surrounded by mountains.

Looking down on to the wide bay with several arms at the head of the Batura, the biggest glacier in this region, we could see more than one exit to the north, but neither to the right nor to the left of our col

---

[*]   Mr and Mrs Bullock-Workman.

was there any way of reaching them; the only way out of the impasse was to go back. Moving one at a time we stepped gingerly down the first 200 ft. where the midday sun was rapidly clearing the thin snow support from the steps we had cut coming up. Then in deeper, safer snow we plunged swiftly to the bergschrund. Gyr continued his plunging a shade too long and fell in. It was not very deep so that he was able to climb out the other side. I decided to jump, but foolishly neglecting to learn from Gyr what the landing was like I lit on ice, slipped, and hit the ground a hearty smack with the back of my head. At first I thought my thick skull had suffered no harm, but by the time we had reached the top of the ice-fall headache and vomiting had set in. In my condition the descent of the ice-fall, the crossing of the lightly bridged crevasses, more dangerous now by the softening snow, and the long trudge back, made our return a slow and dreary business. Two Sherpas came out to carry me the last half-mile and when we reached camp at 4 p.m. I turned in and slept solidly till six o'clock next morning.

I woke more or less cured and breakfasted heartily on the very fine supper I had missed the night before—a spaghetti and another of Angdawa's rhubarb pies. Our last shot in the locker was the low easy col to the west which we had noticed on the way up and which we little doubted would lead us to the Karumbar valley. Except that it would take more time this route would be no less satisfactory or interesting than the other. We could continue up the Karumbar to the Chillinji pass whence Secord could turn west for Chitral, while we others crossed the pass and went down the Chapursan to meet the Mir of Hunza's man who by this time would probably be a little tired of waiting for us. By going this way we might also clear up the mystery of the unexplored gap between the heads of the Kukuay and the Koz Yaz glaciers.

Accordingly we packed up and went down to Little Darakush. Neither Kappeler nor Angtingit were well so, while two of us remained to help with the loads, Secord pushed on to see if there was any suitable camp up the tributary glacier. He found that, though the grass shelf of Little Darakush continued round the corner for some way, except on the glacier itself there was nowhere any water. He had gone nearly to the foot of the ice-fall and reported that the col looked quite near but that the ice-fall might prove troublesome. That afternoon there was a halo round the sun, but its evil promise was not fulfilled until twenty-four hours later, when there was a fierce thunderstorm.

The reconnaissance party left at five o'clock next morning. In one hour we reached the foot of the ice-fall, which was short but steep and quite the blackest and ugliest I have ever seen. The best line seemed to be on our right, where the ice met the rock-wall. Both were so black that it was difficult to say where the ice ended and the rock began. Despite its repulsive aspect Secord and I advanced light-heartedly to the assault and had hardly taken the first few tentative steps up a rock-scoop overhung by a wall of ice when a stone the size of a football whistled down, missing my head by inches and catching Secord fair and square on the forearm. At first we feared it might be broken but, although this did not prove to be the case, he had to be escorted back to camp by Kappeler.

Gyr and I then crossed to the other side. There was a corridor between ice and rock but it was from our point of view a hopeless chasm, difficult to get into and impossible to get out of, and made even more repellent by water streaming into it from the rocks. We then went back to the middle, where the fall of a succession of seracs had flattened out a sort of roadway. Up this we made rapid but fearful progress. The ice was unbelievably rotten and we tacked from side to side seeking but failing to avoid the poised and weighty threat of many tottering seracs. I used to smile at the accounts of very early mountaineers, whose guides imposed on them strict silence when passing close to seracs lest some careless but violent 'Damn' might suffice to bring down a serac on top of the whole party; but I confess it was in complete silence and with bated breath that I passed within range of these leering towers of soft, dripping, honey-combed ice. We were through the worst and the slope had begun to ease as we approached the plateau above the ice-fall. The crevasses became more uniform, more clean-cut, wider and deeper. Success seemed assured when suddenly we were confronted by a series of monster cracks which split the ice from side to side, from one rock-wall to the other. Through, round, or over them, there was no way.

As we retreated, losing our way several times in the labyrinth of cracks, cliffs, and pinnacles, we worked over to the rocks above the scene of the first mishap. There was a way there all right, but it could

In Jaglot village

Men of Chalt—the Lambardar on the left

Bridge near hot spring above Chalt—Rakaposhi in background

The hot spring

only be reached by means of the rock-scoop under the cliff from which stones were now falling frequently as the heat of the sun released them from their ice-bed. Perhaps, if the nights had been cold enough this route might have been used, but it would have been a black business in every way and now with three sick men in the party it was not to be thought of.

Our defeat was complete. There seemed to be no way now of saving anything from the wreck of our hopes. Time was running short, so that even if all the party had been fit neither Secord nor myself could have remained looking for another way over to the Karumbar. Before this was discovered we might easily have found ourselves as far south as the known route by the Daintar nallah below Bar. Our time had not been wasted, however. We had explored the Kukuay from snout to source and it was our misfortune that in so doing we had dissolved our own dreams as well as the draughtsman's. The foundations of our airy castle had collapsed. That dream bubble was pricked, and it was time to acknowledge that 'things are what they are and the consequences will be what they will be', of which the most unpleasant for us was the long dreary march back down the glacier without the buoyancy of novelty and hope which had animated us on the way up. Neither was there any balm for our hurts in the thought of our far from impressive return to Chalt, nor in the remembrance of the Mir's patient emissary watching and wondering at some high alp in the Chapursan.

Painful ordeals of any kind, from a visit to the dentist to a wedding reception, cannot be too soon over. We determined that our sufferings would at any rate be brief, so that two days to Chalt was all we allowed ourselves. We started at 8 a.m. and except for a halt of two hours walked all day until 6 p.m., steering a direct course across the big bend of the glacier for the sheepfold at Aldarkush. All of it was exasperatingly rough going, but although we were clear of the glacier by 5 p.m. we went on until we camped a mile below its junction with the Baltar. We had another casualty when Gyr slipped and cut his hand badly on a stone.

On the 25th we set out for Chalt. Since Angtingit was now unable to carry and travelled slowly even without a load we sent him off early. The rest of us had not been going long before we met him walking back towards us looking even more glum than his sickness would warrant. He reported that the swollen river had overflowed a short piece of the track and that there was no way round. There was certainly no way over, for the river was now in roaring spate and it looked as if we should have to go back to the glacier snout to cross and then find a way down the other side. However, beyond a wide talus of mud and stone, the result of a landslip, there was a steep cliff of hard mud and rock mixed, traversed by a sloping narrow ledge. Beyond this, if we could cross and descend again, was dry land and the track. The man of Bar and I climbed up to and across the traverse and found a way down at the other end, the Bar man leading and hacking steps in the mud with a borrowed ice-axe. It was an exposed place and it was no consolation to know that if one did come off one would only fall into the river. The crossing of the talus was even more perilous, for stones and boulders were shooting down this frequently and rapidly. We carried the loads over, with both eyes on the slope above as a batsman stealing a run watches the fielder. Not one of the Sherpas would take his load across the traverse, but the man of Bar performed prodigies of work and sure-footedness in carrying every load himself.

This caused some delay, but by midday we were eating our lunch at Bar, whence, having hired three coolies to help, we made a push for Chalt. Robinson Crusoe, hearing of our arrival and then of our departure, pursued us almost to the hot springs to offer hospitality, but we were firm and pressed on. Our bathe was welcome, for these springs are reputed to cure all ills and at least three of our party stood in need of their healing waters. At Budelas our mad career was checked for a while by the irresistible desire to gaze long and wonderingly at Rakaposhi. This time it was bright with the glories of a setting sun; but in a short time sky, snow, and shadow mingled, and the spell broke. We reached Chalt as night fell, and for two hours our Sherpas and coolies dribbled in one by one.

That night at Chalt was our last together. Very early next morning Secord departed on his thirty-two mile march to Gilgit where, as we heard, he duly arrived, dead from the feet up but still standing; and a little later, accompanied appropriately enough by one donkey, I left for Misgar and the north.

Though it was the last night, no bottles were cracked (perhaps the 'Ovosport' had run out) and no speeches either of farewell or of recrimination made. Nevertheless, as I lay out under the stars, 'chewing the cud of sweet and bitter fancy', I paid a silent tribute to these companions with whom the adventure had originated, who had shared equally and uncomplainingly both the worries of preparation, the more bearable physical troubles of realization, and in the end the keen disappointment of failure. In particular they had submitted to a certain amount of dictation which was often unexplained or, by reason of language difficulties, inexplicable. On many occasions they had had good reason to exclaim with Omar:

> What, without asking, hither hurried whence?
> And, without asking, whither hurried hence?
> Another and another cup to drown
> The memory of this impertinence.

German or French have I none. My English is neither clear nor pure, yet in spite of, or because, perhaps, of these language barriers, harsh words, though they may have been thought, were seldom uttered. Climbing parties of mixed nationalities are not always harmonious, and tempers are more tried by defeat than by success, but possibly the reason that our party had been so happy was that Swiss and English are as near in outlook as different nations can expect to be. Above all, our respective attitudes to mountains and mountaineering are pretty much the same.

As for our crushing defeat by Rakaposhi, while not wishing to diminish the part played by the mountain in bringing this about, I think our chief mistake was in attempting the climb too early in the season. This was largely my fault for having arranged to leave for Kashgar in July. To devote less than two months to a big unknown mountain is bordering on disrespect, and if the mountain be a Rakaposhi then two objectives in one season are too much. Whether either of our two routes would be easier later in the year is unlikely, but they would undoubtedly be less dangerous. Though July's weather was by no means perfect it was better than that of June. Later still there would, of course, be less snow to avalanche and perhaps the cornices would be less formidable.

Our ignoring of other ways and our gamble on the Jaglot approach seems to have been justified, for in August the Swiss had a look at the north side and the Bagrot nallah and in their opinion our approach, such as it was, was the best—probably the only one worth trying. Had we carried out our first plan of reconnoitring every side we should have got nowhere. In the Himalaya it seems to be almost impossible to tell whether a given route will go without trying it, and to do this on a high mountain is prodigal of time. Judgement, I repeat, is, perhaps, the greatest mountaineering asset of all, and though our difficulty in judging routes may have reflected on ourselves, it nevertheless confirmed the truth of Dr Longstaff's dictum which I have already quoted, that in the Himalaya the only certain proof of a route is to try it.

Whether our judgement in abandoning the two routes we did try was also at fault I cannot tell. Who shall draw the line between prudence and pusillanimity? Prudence, as Dr Johnson tells us, 'Quenches that ardour of enterprise by which everything is done that can claim praise or admiration, and represses that generous temerity which often fails and often succeeds.' To which I shall only add that in mountaineering one man's prudence is another man's poison.

CHAPTER IX

CHALT TO MISGAR

———◆———

FOR MANY PEOPLE distant places have a peculiar form of magnet-
ism which grows as the distance increases. I am thus attracted, and
besides its remoteness there is for me a strange thrill in the mere sound
of Chinese Turkestan, situated as it is in the heart of Central Asia where
place-names like Kashgar, Yarkand, Urumchi, awaken half-forgotten
memories of Marco Polo and the old Silk Road linking Peking and
Samarkand; of Turkomans and Kirghiz; of rich camel caravans and
mud-walled caravanserais. There, too, are the Takla Makan desert, the
grave alike of great rivers and of cities of an ancient civilization, and
the Pamirs, the so-called Roof of the World, that strange barren region
where the three Empires of Great Britain, Russia, and China once met.

Many travellers have succumbed to the lure of Chinese Turkestan
or Sinkiang as it is now known: Shaw, Dalgliesh (murdered near Yarkand), Bower, Forsyth, Hayward (murdered in Chitral), Trotter, Dau-
vergne, in the last century, and in more recent times Younghusband,
Sven Hedin, and the late Sir Aurel Stein, who did more than anyone
to increase our knowledge of Central Asia. These men, more especially
the earlier travellers, had danger to face and real difficulties to overcome, for owing to the extreme lawlessness which prevailed they travelled as often as not in peril of their lives. But at the end of last century
and the beginning of this the heyday of Central Asian travel dawned.
By then order had been established and any man, even one who was
neither a scientist nor an official, could wander alone and unarmed,
except for a passport, facing nothing more serious than the ordinary
hardships of travel. Now, however, the pendulum has swung to the
other extreme. Hardship and peril are to seek, but law and order have
between them generated official obstruction and any would-be traveller must first overleap its wellnigh impassable barrier.

Ever since it was established (1890) the British Consulate at Kashgar has been a refuge, a home, and a base for travellers in Sinkiang,

and some time ago the present (1947) Consul, Mr E. E. Shipton, had invited me to join him in a climbing holiday. The project was one of many months' standing, but although we live enmeshed like flies in a cobweb world of plans—mostly on a five-year basis—all plans, particularly those of individuals, become of necessity more and more tentative. Fresh circumstances, some new regulation, civil commotion, or rumours of war, cause them to be recast or scrapped almost as soon as made, so that it was with relief and surprise that I found myself actually on the point of starting out for Kashgar; the more so since Sinkiang, isolated though it is, has been in recent years in the same state of nervous effervescence as the rest of the world. Even while we were on Rakaposhi I had read in a paper of disturbances there.

Very early in our acquaintance, the Sherpas had made it clear that none of them had the wish or the intention to go with me. I attributed this either to their dislike of me or to their fear of the fatal attraction of Kashgar, for a Sherpa who had gone there with Mr Shipton in 1941 had never returned, but had settled, married (or contracted a liaison), and prospered. I was therefore alone for the first part of my journey to Misgar, the last post on the British side of the border, where I was to meet a man sent down by Shipton. Having hastily packed a few things, seen Secord start, admonished the Sherpas to behave themselves, and said good-bye, I took the road with my donkey. The road passes through Budelas and then follows the right bank of the Hunza river to its source near the Mintaka pass. Travellers are few, but I met a Punjabi who had strayed rather far from his parish, and to him I was able to give a note for the Swiss asking them to send on a climbing rope which I had forgotten. At Maiun, opposite Nilt, I changed my slow-moving donkey for a coolie. We were in Hunza proper now and I noticed at once how much more obliging, business-like, and tractable the people were than those around Gilgit. Many of the men were ex-soldiers of the Indian Army and if one of them was about I was always well served.

That night we slept at Hini in a dusty shack which was the school by day and the rest-house by night. Hini is a big village which suffers from water shortage, and had it not been for the unusual rain this summer the crops would have been in a poor way. As all these villages depend on irrigation, rain, if it comes at all in summer, is not often welcomed, for in June the apricots will be spread to dry, in July the lucerne will be cut, and in August the wheat will be ripe. Provided the water supply comes from a substantial glacier the farmer, and even his children's children, may face the future with confidence, but should it come merely from high snow-beds which must be replenished every winter, then these people are as completely at the mercy of the weather as farmers elsewhere. The feelings of these water-starved Hinians must have been daily harrowed by the sight of two enormous streams pouring down from the Minapin glacier to waste their goodness on the fields of the despised and hated Nagars just across the river.

In Hunza territory there is a system by which coolies must be changed every few miles. Whether the change takes an hour as it sometimes does, or much less, such delay is maddening to anyone in a hurry. But no one should hurry in the East—that no man hurries except when catching flies is a proverb with a far wider application than Egypt its home, and Kipling, too, has some advice for the would-be hustler:

> And the end of the fight is a tombstone white
> > with the name of the late deceased,
> And the epitaph drear: 'A fool lies here who tried to hustle the East.'

The time taken to change coolies depends on whether the lambardar of the village is within easy reach, how far his voice carries, and whether or no his selected victim is within earshot. Between Hini and Baltit, the capital of Hunza and the Mir's residence, I had three of these changes to make. A few miles from Baltit the road meets and follows the great Berber 'kul' alongside which one walks in the comforting assurance that water will not flow uphill. This, the one day which I wanted to be fine, was not; lowering clouds obscured the Minapin glacier and shut out the whole northern face of Rakaposhi which I had hoped so much to see. On the way I met a brother of the Mir bound for Gilgit; the Mir himself was away in Srinagar, but all arrangements for my comfort had been made at the guest-house in the Palace grounds.

On the other side of the river is Nagar territory. The capital, Nagar, lies about five miles up the Nagar river from its junction with the Hunza river just below Baltit. Though they are such close neighbours and though they seem to come of the same stock and to speak a similar language the people of the two states have never been on good terms. The Hunza are Maulais, followers of the Aga Khan, while the Nagar are Shiahs. On one occasion only have the two states agreed and that was in 1891 when a British force was obliged to occupy both states in order to enforce a more rigid observance of their agreement to forego their old custom of raiding on the Karakoram trade route between Leh and Yarkand. The then Mir of Hunza fled to Sinkiang and Muhammad Nazim Khan, his half-brother, reigned in his stead until his death in 1938. His autobiography is one of the books to be seen in the guest-house. There has long been a vague connection between Hunza, or Kanjut as the Chinese call it, and Chinese Turkestan. The Mir claims the Taghdumbash Pamir north of the Hindu Kush and now exercises grazing rights there for which he pays an annual but nominal tribute of gold dust to the Chinese.

The exceptional health, vitality, and cheerfulness of the Hunza, and their superiority in these respects over their neighbours, has long been recognised by all who have had anything to do with them except, of course, by those aforesaid neighbours. It has been made a matter for study and for speculation and has been variously attributed either to the climatic conditions or to merely their way of life and mode of culti-vation. One theory is that since they live on the northern slopes of the valley they enjoy more sun, but those who have lived among and have had opportunities of studying the Hunza maintain that their almost perfect health is owing principally to their food and above all to the way such food is grown. Sir Robert McCarrison, C.L.E., a nutrition expert with long experience of India, who lived as a doctor among the Hunza; Dr G.T. Wrench, who also lived with them and wrote about them in a book, *The Wheel of Health*; and Mrs Lorimer, who made a study of their language (see *Language Hunting in the Karakoram*), while living with them, are in agreement on this matter and lay particular stress on the 'wholeness' of their system of agriculture—every scrap of vegetable matter, all organic waste that comes from the soil is put back in the form of compost. Of them and their system of terrace cul-tivation Dr L.J. Picton has written in *Thoughts on Feeding*: 'Somehow their life, seemingly hard and austere, has endowed these people with a happiness I forbear to overstate. They have achieved engineering without mathematics, morality without moralising, agriculture with-out chemistry, health without medicine, sufficiency without trade. In the harsh and unpromising surroundings of the Hunza, mastery of the art of life has been engendered by an unremitting agriculture.' Their diet consists of wheat bread (I can testify to its deliciousness), a little milk and its products, vegetables, lentils, mulberries, and in particular their great stand-by, apricots. These are their only source of sugar, and the stones of the apricot are ground to extract the oil which is their one illuminant. The dried fruit is their principal winter provision. While one is willing to concede that this way of living will go most of the way towards ensuring health and vitality, it does not explain their superiority in these respects over their neighbours, whose diet and method of agriculture are substantially the same. None of these neighbouring peoples has been or is likely to be picked out as the embodiment of perfect health and well-being. Perhaps the more robust character and industry of the Hunza is accounted for by the poverty of their country, which in the three great needs of arable land, water, and wood, is less well off than any of the neighbouring territories. As well as in manliness and husbandry they excel as craftsmen. As carpenters, masons, ironsmiths, builders of roads, bridges, or flumes, they are superior to their neighbours; even their home-spun cloth is a better article. It rather looks as though in spite of the similarity of appearance, habits, and language they and the Nagar do come of a different racial stock. Col. R. C. F. Schomberg, who knows as much about the people of these parts as anyone, thinks that the Nagar is a mixture of Balti, Gilgiti, and, later, Dogra blood, and is quite distinct from that of Hunza. The Hunza themselves claim to have come originally from Badakshan, and the theory that they are descendants of some of Alexander the Great's soldiers is, I suppose, no more far-fetched than some theories of racial descent.

A few miles from Baltit, on a cliff overhanging the Hunza river, is the village and castle of Altit—once the northern limit of Hunza territory. At the present time the state extends as far as the Hindu Kush, although not all the intervening villages are occupied by Hunza folk for many Wakhis from Wakhan, in Afghanistan, have settled there. From Altit the track narrows and deteriorates as well it might, for the valley of the Hunza river now becomes an almost continuous gorge, cut on a scale to daunt the most resolute road builder. To Gulmit, a stage of twenty-two miles, every mile of a devilish loose, rough, up-and-down track lies in a uniformly stark and barren canon. Sometimes, when the water is low, it drops to the river-bed to take advantage of a brief stretch of sand or gravel flat. Other times it climbs dizzily to cross some perpendicular precipice by means of ingeniously constructed galleries. Before and behind, the traveller's view is limited to the short livid-grey reach of water between one frequent bend and another, and on either hand by leaden cliffs or long sombre slopes of scree. The sense of confinement induced by the long passage through the gorge is only momentarily relieved by glimpses of the bright fields of Gulmit, happily situated on a wide, sunny, well-watered alluvial fan where every available scrap of land boasted either the fresh green lucerne, yellowing wheat, or pink-white buckwheat.

From Gulmit to Pasu is but nine miles and though to the traveller the tedium of the gorge may be relieved, its savageness is enhanced by the entrance of two glaciers, the Ghulkin and the Pasu, which the track skirts. Near the snout of the former I estimated the moraine to be nearly 500 ft. high. Immediately beyond and within a mile of the ice of the Pasu is the village of the same name. It is a Wakhi village and is reputed to grow the finest apples in the country. I tasted them and was disappointed, but I met with a new bread made with fat in it which is excellent to eat and keeps well.

Above Pasu the track crosses the great Batura glacier, the head of which, twenty-five miles to the west, we had looked down upon nine days before. It took me nearly an hour to cross the ice, which flows down almost to the water of the Hunza river. Like most Himalayan glaciers it is at present slowly retreating; in 1930 the snout actually reached the river. This year when I crossed the track was easy, but naturally it varies from year to year, so that animals have often to make a wide detour round the snout or, in former years, to cross the river and back again. Just before reaching the glacier one notices, on the other side of the river, the forbidding entrance to the Shingshal gorge, up which lies a difficult route to the upper Yarkand valley and the Leh-Yarkand road. This was one of the routes favoured by Hunza raiders, especially in winter when the shrunken state of the river allowed the use of the river-bed as a road.

The next village beyond the Batura glacier is Khaibar, thirteen miles from Pasu. It was the rule at these villages, as it is in most out-of-the-way places which happen to lie on a trade route, for the incoming

The 'mud traverse'—two Sherpas can be seen immediately below upper edge of picture left centre

Robinson Crusoe

Rock tower (*c.* 21,000 ft.) on Kukuay-Batura watershed

The ice-fall which defeated us: scene of Secord's mishap is where ice meets rock on right. The 'low snow col' is off the picture to the right

traveller to become the centre of a news-hungry circle of inquirers. Julius Caesar remarked of the Gauls: 'It is a habit of theirs to stop travellers and inquire whatsoever each of them may have heard or known about any sort of matter; the common people beset the passing trader, demanding to hear from what regions he came, what things he got acquainted with there.' And so it was 2000 years later at Pasu where, as I ate my eggs and bread, I was asked to make known whatsoever news and views I had. It is at any rate a pleasing change to have news that is not common to all and to have people listen with respect to one's callow views on world affairs; and as such things are acceptable, to give them in full measure is but a slight return to make for hospitality received. While this time-honoured custom was being observed two men carrying loads joined the circle. I thought the loads looked familiar, and presently I discovered they were the two I had dispatched to Misgar from Gilgit. They had been taken up the Chapursan nallah to meet us, but as we had not arrived they were now on their way back to Gilgit.

In the afternoon I went on the remaining five miles to Malkhun accompanied by one coolie, one donkey, and one madman, to carry my new and heavy acquisitions. It was a comparatively pleasant march. The gorge began slightly to relent, the road became easier, the vista wider, the scenery a shade milder, and, as one who considers himself a rugged mountaineer, unappalled by the most savage rock scenery so long as he is safe at its foot, I'm ashamed to say I felt it a relief. We are in the habit of smiling at the childish fears and fancies of eighteenth-century writers when they came upon a mountain scene. The matter-of-fact Defoe, for instance, who writes of the 'high and formidable Hills of Cumberland with a kind of unhospitable Terror in them', and of Westmorland as 'the wildest, most barren, and Frightful of any that I have passed over'—I cannot help wondering what he would have written and how many capital letters he would have employed to describe three or four days' imprisonment in the Hunza gorge. I confess that by the time I began to emerge, the wild intractable savagery of the scene had become overpowering and depressing.

Malkhun is a very small village. Instead of the usual large audience there were but two men and a boy to watch the stranger eat his evening meal of eggs, bread, 'lassi' or curds, and a vegetable of the spinach variety very nicely cooked in butter by the lambardar's wife. Here, as in every village I had passed, they asked earnestly for quinine which, as malaria is unknown, they must eat as a sweet—hard men with acrid tastes as befits their inexorably harsh home. The gorge had relented, but only for a moment. Above Malkhun it became nearly as morose and inhuman as before, but now an otherwise stern scene was gladdened by the river, which lost its livid glacier-fed complexion to become a cheerful sparkling blue, while here and there a handsome heliotrope weed (called, I was told, 'phobshing') brightened the bleak monotony of rock and rubble slopes.

Misgar, which I reached on the afternoon of 31 July, is on a wide sunny shelf lying well above the river. Despite the height of 10,000 ft. wheat grows well. I pitched my tent in a field by the Post Office, the last link in the telegraph line to Gilgit, where I was soon discovered by Naiad Shah, the Hunza man whom Shipton had sent from Tashkurghan to meet me. He was a wiry little man, lame in one foot, with the sad earnest inquiring expression of a Cairn terrier which, indeed, he closely resembled. He told me he spoke four languages besides his own, Burishaski, which is that spoken in Hunza, Nagar, and Yasin, and which is without affinity to any other. Turki, Persian, Wakhi, and Hindustani, were his other four, but it seemed to me that at times he was not quite clear which of the five he was using.

Shipton, who employs a number of Hunza servants in the Consulate, has his own theory about this much admired race. While admitting in full their qualities of industry, keenness, enterprise, willingness, cheerfulness, and loyalty, he considers this altogether admirable make-up is marred by a lack of intelligence, nous, or gumption—that in the day-to-day business of life they display a sort of bucolic 'dumbness' comparable to that of the good people of Haddenham who built a shed over their village pond to keep the ducks dry, or the shrewd folk of Steeple Bumpstead who rejected a proposal for a second windmill on the grounds that there was barely enough wind for the first. Although my experience of them is small I would not go the whole way with him in this, but I must say that in the short time he was with me Naiad Shah did his best to convince me that Shipton was right. Much of his apparent stupidity may have been owing to language difficulties, for if one asked him how far it was to the next halt he might reply that he had some in his saddle-bags. But it does not argue much intelligence to pack eggs in the bedding and leave them there. Still he looked after me with great faithfulness, and since he was well known and liked all along the road his presence was enough to ensure every available comfort for man and beast.

After breakfasting with the Kashmiri telegraph clerk, a Hindu alone amongst Moslems, Naiad Shah loaded our baggage pony, mounted or rather climbed from a rock on to his own flea-bitten sorrel, and off we went. His mounting difficulties were owing to his lame foot and to the capacious saddlebags which stuck out far enough on either side to make any mounting in the orthodox way impossible. The gorge embraced us once more though now less fiercely, and soon, in the narrowest part of the defile, we passed the fort at Kalam Darchi occupied by a platoon of Gilgit Scouts, the last outpost of British India. On this day, 1 August, the Gilgit Agency was being handed over to the Kashmir State and, although British rule had ended, the Subadar in charge of the fort appeared to be in no hurry to haul down for the last time his Union Jack.

CHAPTER X

MISGAR TO TASHKURGHAN

THE HUNZA RIVER, now little more than a beck, here ran in a wide, deep stony valley. We halted for the night at Murkushi in a setting of grass and birch trees. All around us were snow mountains, and so I was shaken by the sight of two very fat camels contentedly grazing, as unexpected a sight as polar bears in a desert. Later I was frequently to see camels against a background of snow mountains, but so close in one's mind is the association of camels with hot sandy deserts that the apparent incongruity was always striking. These camels are the two-humped Bactrian type with shorter legs and more massive body than the dromedary; great shaggy ruffs of hair on thighs and neck added to their ponderous appearance, so very different from the bald, scraggy beasts one sees dragging carts in Karachi. These two had strayed from a herd belonging to the Mir of Hunza which was grazing up the Kilik nallah. And I was delighted to see them, for though we had reached a pretty remote part of India and turned our backs on the last British outpost, the magic of Central Asia had not yet begun to work. True, Naiad Shah was from across the border, but he was a Hunza man and looked it, about whom there was not a vestige of glamour or mystery.

Murkushi is the starting-point for either the Kilik or the Mintaka passes, which are not many miles apart and are of about the same height, 15,500 ft. In winter the Mintaka is said to carry less snow. The ascent to this pass is gradual except for the last few hundred feet, when the track quits the moraine of a very fine, active-looking glacier to climb a low rounded ridge to the north. Though the ascent is easy the track is for the most part made of boulders. I remarked on this to Naiad Shah, who assured me that on the other side things were better, and left me with the impression that not only did the boulders end on the top but that a grazier's paradise began. That we had already left one region for another was apparent by the character of the low ridge ahead of us, so different from the opposite containing wall of the glacier, where a high rampart of rock buttresses, snow gullies, and tumbled ice-falls culminated in a noble 21,000 ft. peak—a fitting sentinel for the last northwestern bastion of the Karakoram. And so when the pass is crossed, though there is nothing to warn the traveller that he has reached a political boundary, the most myopic could not fail to realise that he had crossed a geological and climatic boundary. In place of the deepcut valleys of the south, filled with rivers of crevassed, wrinkled, grey ice and flanked by high jagged peaks, there are now smooth rounded hills, whose higher summits are crowned with white unblemished slabs of ice, spilling over for a short way into the upper part of wide shallow valleys to end abruptly on the dark scree.

We had some way to go down the northern slope before Naiad Shah's rash promise was fulfilled. I did not count them, but I estimated that for every hundred boulders on the north side there were ninety-nine on this, but by the time we reached the valley-floor the track had indeed become one on which one could walk, trot, or canter with ease and safety. The valley had all the appearance of some high Welsh valley, but on a vast scale. There was no tree, no bush, no lowly shrub to break the sweeping expanse of scree and brown earth. Grass there was, but the blades were so sparsely scattered that even at this time of high summer one's eyes received but the vaguest impression of anything green. This was Naiad Shah's grazier's paradise, but the beasts which live on it—the yaks, camels, sheep, goats—seem to prefer it that way. They love to fossick about on a heap of gravel for rare tufts of grass in the hopeful energetic way of a down-at-heel miner fossicking the tailings of an old mine for specks of gold. Put a yak down in a lush water-meadow up to his knees in grass and he would not know what to do with it. In a short time you would, I think, find him out on the road snuffling happily over a heap of road metal where, if it had been there long enough, a few spare weeds might have struggled into existence. Yaks and camels, both beasts of prodigious strength and size, are a lesson in what dogged persevering browsing can do for one even on the most meagre diet.

Such was my impression, but in reality the grass of the Pamir valleys, though coarse and yellow, is rich and succulent enough to be famous throughout Central Asia. Horses thrive on it. Marco Polo remarks of the Taghdumbash Pamir that it is 'clothed with the finest pasture in the world; insomuch that a lean beast will fatten to your heart's content in ten days'. There are eight of these so-called Pamirs which are merely high shallow valleys, lying at a height of between 10,000 and 15,000 ft., and rounded mountains, some of which carry perpetual snow. Their characteristics are treeless desolation, meandering streams, peaty bottoms, and shallow lakes. The meaning and origin of the word 'Pamir' has been, and perhaps still is, a rich field for conjecture which I am happily not qualified to explore.

The Taghdumbash Pamir lies along the Chinese-Russian frontier from the Wakhjir pass northwards where it merges into the Sarikol range. Below it on the Chinese side lies the spacious valley of the Tashkhurgan river. This country along the western border of Sinkiang is known as Sarikol, the principal town of which is Tashkurghan. In recent years it has been a disturbed area owing to the incursions of troublemakers from the Russian side of the border.

It had been a long day. We had started at 6 a.m. and did not reach the first habitation at Mintaka Karaul until 7 p.m. Here our valley was joined by another coming down from three important passes, the Kilik, the Wakhjir leading to Wakhan, and the Tigurmansu by which there is a way to Kizil Robat in Soviet Turkestan, and at this strategic point there was a mud-walled Chinese fort. The fort was then unoccupied, but hard by were three 'yorts', the circular felt tents of the nomads, at which we were well received by the Tajik owners. These people are semi-nomads who are found mainly in Sarikol. Their mode of life seemed very similar to that of the Kirghiz. The only way I could tell whether my hosts were Kirghiz or Tajik was by the fireplace which in a Tajik 'yort' is a round clay affair about two feet high, whereas the Kirghiz use an open fire. The traveller who has studied books of Central Asian travel will be already aware that the two most important features in the landscape are yaks and yorts, but should he ask to ride on the one or sleep in the other he will be disappointed, for neither seem to be known by those names. 'Ak-oi' is the name of the Kirghiz round dwellings, or 'aoul' for a collection of them, while' koshgau' is the most generally understood word for *Peophagus grunniens*. However, being far from pedantic I shall continue to speak of yaks and yorts, both easy, pronounceable words with a strong Asiatic flavour.

The yort consists of a circular framework of willow sticks about five feet high and fifteen feet diameter, covered first with a reed mat and then with felt. On top of this, curving willow rods support the felt roof, in the centre of which a hole about five feet across serves the dual purpose of window and chimney. At night or in bad weather felts are drawn across this hole by a rope on the outside. In the better yorts the felts are decorated outside with bright patterns and tufts of coloured wool, and are secured inside with wide bands of embroidered loose-woven cloth. Carpets, cushions, and pillows are neatly stacked round one-half of the inside wall while a mat partition in one corner screens off the larder and dairy. Here they keep meat and milk, and the enormous copper pans and other utensils for turning the milk into butter and 'joghrat'. Three yaks can carry a yort and its furniture.

'Joghrat' is Wood's (the famous explorer of the Oxus sources) spelling for the curdled milk of the nomads, which seems to be the same word and the same stuff as the Bulgarian 'yoghourt'. The Albanian 'Kos' and the Afghan 'Mos' is the same thing. This is the food popularly supposed to be responsible for the extreme longevity of many Bulgars and Turks. In those countries centenarians are two a penny and they attribute their health and length of life to their earnest devotion to 'yoghourt', just as our more infrequent centenarians attribute their success to either beer or total abstinence. In a few restaurants in London a jar of 'yoghourt' the size of a large tea-cup can be bought for ninepence, but in a yort a bowl of the stuff the size of a wash-basin is put down in front of the guest or odd caller to keep him quiet until tea is brewed. In appearance it resembles junket, and it can be swallowed in the same easy absent-minded way, but its taste is sharp and slightly acid. If there are three or four wooden spoons at work the bowl is soon emptied and it is then replaced by a larger one. I had my own spoon, but in many yorts there seemed to be only one with which each man of the circle took a mouthful and then passed it to his neighbour. Sipping is not quite the word, but unlike port there are no rules for dealing with 'yoghourt', the spoon can be passed either way.

Naiad Shah and I stretched ourselves luxuriously on felt rugs, propped and cushioned with pillows, while between us a bowl that had just been dredged of 'yoghourt' was replaced by a large copper teapot. The Tajik men and boys sat or squatted, smoking our cigarettes and peering at us out of little pig-eyes from under their great hairy caps. The Tajik women worked. Obviously mutton was to be the main supper dish, but I took more interest in another which was in preparation. A lump of dough was rolled out to the shape of a very thin disk three feet across on a bit of flat board less than half that size. Under less skilled hands a lot of the earth floor and a quantity of carpet would have adhered to the dough long before it had reached the desired acreage. The thin disk was then smeared liberally with clotted cream, cut into strips, and the whole wound up into a round flat loaf which was then baked. The result was a pastry of angelic flakiness, saturated but not sodden with cream, which oozed gratefully from the corners of the mouth as the flakes melted in it. It was a rich meal.

> We cleansed our beards of the mutton grease,
> We lay on our mats and were filled with peace.

And as we did so a youth played a three-stringed fiddle in one corner, Naiad Shah related the latest lies from Misgar, our host spread his mat to pray on one side of us, while on the other our hostess bared her breasts to feed her youngest baby. I felt I had been made free of Central Asia.

We rode on down the valley in an easterly direction with the Taghdumbash Pamir on our left until we saw the dust of an approaching cavalcade. This proved to be the 'beg' or headman from Beyik who had come to welcome us, and he was presently followed by the Tajik commander of the police post with an armed escort. The Beyik post watches the road to the Beyik pass to Russian territory a day's march away, but this pass like all the others between Sinkiang and Russia is now closed. Politeness obliged us to drink tea at the small fort where only something far more compelling would have persuaded us to stay. The police quarters, doorless and windowless, lined the inside walls, on top of which stood a sentry sourly eyeing the blank uninspiring landscape. The commandant's room, as sparsely furnished as a hermit's cell, smelt like a slum or a disused dug-out. A piece of fish skewered to one wall and a mutton bone to the other were the only concession to interior decoration. The walls of the fort positively oozed 'cafard' and although this small force of Tajik police had only been in residence nine months one would have guessed from their moss-grown appearance that the period had been much longer. No formalities were required, but I felt that already the free air of the Pamirs was slightly tainted with officialdom and I wondered what kind of reception we should receive from the first real Chinese official whom we were due to meet next day at Dafdar.

Seven miles down from Beyik the valley bends north and is joined by the valley of the Oprang river from the south. At the junction there is a small settlement where barley is grown despite the height of nearly 12,000 ft. The serious obstacle presented by the Oprang had to be over-come with the help of two men from the settlement who came to our assistance with a horse as high as a camel in order to keep our loads out of the water. While the men thawed their frozen legs we ate barley bread fresh from the oven. The flat cake, leavened with sour dough from the previous baking and sprinkled with milk on one side and water on the other, is slapped on to the clay wall of the fire-place which has been well hotted up with yak dung fuel. When baked it peels read-ily off the wall.

Our next halt was at the long straggling Wakhi colony of Dafdar on a flat by the river where fields of wheat and barley extend for sev-eral miles. Water for irrigation is led from springs seeping out between the flat and the foot of the slope. Most of the square flat-roofed mud houses were unoccupied, as their owners stay with their herds until the autumn when the crops are ripe. Outside each house was a little clump of willows, the first trees I had seen in Sinkiang. We quartered ourselves in a yort on the outskirts where we were soon visited by the Chinese lieutenant and an interpreter from the fort about a mile away. He was the conventional looking Chinaman of the young student type, complete with horn-rimmed spectacles, full of affability and polite-ness. A mark of politeness which nowadays is often overlooked, espe-cially by those whose minds run on forms and questionnaires and by enthusiastic amateurs of general statistical information, is to refrain from asking personal questions. The lieutenant asked nothing, not even for my passport, but he did threaten to post a sentry over the yort and its valuable occupant and also to see that the occupant had a hot bath at the fort in the morning.

Both threats were carried out. At the fort I found the whole pla-toon of about thirty men had been turned into stokers and boilermen, and I had no option but to get into the long narrow tin coffin which seemed to be one of the few pieces of barrack furniture allowed in the Chinese army. The lieutenant's room was as austerely furnished as the Tajik policeman's—table, chairs, bed—bare of books, papers, or pictures, not even a pin-up girl or a piece of fish to brighten the mud walls. I felt sorry for this youth from Chunking shut up here in control of thirty men as devoid of occupation as himself. He had no interest in shooting, climbing, or even travelling, which are three of the more obvious diversions the country can offer. These troops had newly arrived from China proper, where no doubt they had had experience of war and judging by their looks they had not quite got over it. In a town, well-turned-out soldiers with nothing to do grate on the senses only slightly less than do slovenly ones, but in a wild, barely inhabited landscape any soldier at all is an eyesore; particularly when, as here, having neither parades nor training to attend, he sees the sun rise with no other hope than that he will fill his belly before it sets.

Between Dafdar and Tashkurghan there are two hateful stages across stone and gravel plains whose almost complete sterility is only broken by a small patch of sweet short grass at Taghlak Gumbaz. A 'gumbaz' is of very common occurrence in Sinkiang and Wakhan. It is a tomb or a monument to commemorate the name of some holy man, made generally of mud brick, or clay and gravel, and shaped like a beehive which has outgrown its strength. It is set on a low square foundation in which a single door, never more than three feet high, seems built mainly to discourage entrance; but I imagine that a 'gumbaz' is intended to shelter travellers who thus will be reminded of their benefactor whose name it commemorates.

On this occasion we were not obliged to make use of its rather sepulchral interior, for close by there was an unoccupied yort. We reached it early in the afternoon, and the wretched horses, according to the custom of the country, were then tied up short with their heads in a position of constraint instead of being turned loose to drink and graze. There they remained until sundown, when they were freed. This system of horse-mastership is wrong according to our ideas, but all—Kirghiz, Tajik, Turkoman, and Chinese—affirm that it is harmful to horses to allow them to eat or drink immediately after a journey. In spite of my protests Naiad Shah strongly supported this heresy. One reason he gave was that, apart from ill-effects, a horse so treated is sure to graze all night instead of wasting his time in sleep. Nor will these people allow their horses to drink on the march, though sometimes when crossing streams it is as much as they can do to urge the thirsty beasts across.

Between this 'gumbaz' and Tashkurghan, in what is now perfect desert, many traces of old abandoned fields can be seen. According to Sir Aurel Stein, these were once watered by an ancient canal known as 'Farhad's Canal', parts of which are still visible along the hillside. For hours a white blur in the distance across the river shimmered unchangingly in the heat haze, seeming to defy our approach. That, I concluded, must be Tashkurghan, the ancient capital of Sarikol. Far beyond it, very faint and dimly white in the loess* haze, rose a great dome—Muztagh Ata.

---

* A very fine porous yellowish loam. Loess deposits are remarkable for their capacity to retain vertical walls in the banks of streams. Such walls are characteristic of the scenery around Kashgar.

CHAPTER XI

MUZTAGH ATA

I N A TENT IN THE GARDEN of the Postal Superintendent (a Hunza
man) I found the Consul and his wife. They were on an extended
tour and had arrived the previous evening. In most countries I
associate consuls with long flights of stairs at the top of which is
an office with a locked door and a small printed card bearing the
legend 'Consulate of Utopia—Office hours, Saturdays only, 10–12',
and it struck me that in Kashgar a consul must be an even rarer
bird of passage. The answer is, however, that here the British Consul
being no mere parochial stamper of passports is expected to travel
about and, like the sun, to shed his beneficent rays over the whole
of Kashgaria. Tashkurghan, the capital of Sarikol, is also a receiving and dispatching centre on the mail route to India and is therefore important enough to deserve official attention. If then by any
chance his return journey were to lie in the direction of Muztagh
Ata the Chinese of all people would be the last to demur; for did
not Confucius say: 'The wise find pleasure in waters, the virtuous in
mountains': and again the epigrams of Chang Ch'ao tell us: 'If there
are no famous hills then nothing need be said, but since there are,
they must be visited.'

In former days Tashkurghan must have been a town of some
importance, for it lies on one of the two ancient routes from China to
Western Asia and the Persian Gulf. Two very great travellers, Marco
Polo and the Chinese Buddhist pilgrim Hsuan-tsang (c. A.D. 600)
must have visited it. Nowadays it is only of secondary importance,
for the bulk of what trade there is with India goes by the Leh route.
A lifeless bazaar, some serais usually empty, the modern Chinese fort
and magistracy, and the ruins of the walled town of earlier days, are
all it can boast. But its proximity to the Russian frontier, across which
there is a pass less then twenty miles south-west of the town, makes it
of some interest to the Chinese, who have installed a small garrison.

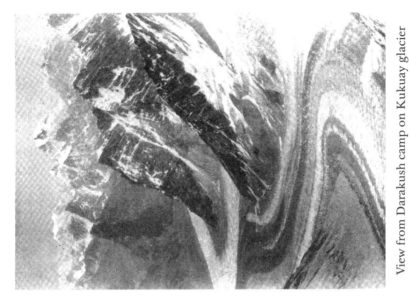

View from Darakush camp on Kukuay glacier

Looking down to the Batura glacier from Kukuay col

Easy going on 'dry' ice of upper Kukuay glacier

The ice-fall leading to Kukuay col—route lies up snow corridor and
behind rock spur right centre of picture

In 1946 the local 'nationalists', with assistance from over the border, took and held Tashkurghan for some time.

Before we could start for Muztagh Ata the duties of hospitality had to be discharged. The Amban and the officers of the garrison invited us to lunch and, since we were in haste to be off, the Consul insisted that they should give us our revenge by dining with us the same day. The Chinese custom of multiplying the courses of a meal almost to infinity is well known, and though the resources of Tashkurghan did not give our hosts the scope they would have wished they did their best and we had to deal seriatim with the following: by way of limbering up there was tea with brandy butter in it, cake and apples; then meat patties, meat balls, fried eggs and radishes, roast mutton, liver, duck, local fish, soup, and rice, the last being the accepted way of delivering the *coup de grâce* at these feasts. Chopsticks, knives, spoons, forks, and fingers, were all brought into play according to the toughness of the opposition, and the whole was eased down with 'kumiss', fermented mare's milk—colourless, slightly alcoholic, sour, and reminiscent of cider. The uncultured yahoo when he gives a feast (and I prefer it his way) merely increases the amount of the ordinary meal. Instead of a few scraggy bones, one or two sheep are dished up, instead of a bowl of rice or pilau, a bucket of it; but civilized people like the Romans, the Chinese, and to a lesser extent ourselves, like to measure their social status by the number and variety of the courses, which I consider a barbaric habit, destructive to the stomach and inimical to good cooking.

One of the principal difficulties in entertaining a posse of Chinese officials (Mrs Shipton had fourteen to cope with) is to get them inside the room. Questions of precedence lead to what threatens to be an interminable contest of polite diffidence until it is cut short by the pressure from behind of those whose claims are too lowly to be worth disputing and whose hunger is too sharp to be any longer denied. The posse surges forward, and when the less nimble have picked themselves up from the floor the contest is renewed over the question of seating. It was a pretty motley assortment that eventually got themselves sat down—one which was difficult to weld into a convivial whole, aided though it was by Russian brandy and Shipton's manful sallies into the unchartered intricacies of Chinese, of which he had enough to excite my admiration and to fascinate the Chinese. Most Chinese are abstemious to a fault. Only the Amban and a man who claimed to have accompanied Sir Aurel Stein on some of his journeys (in the capacity of coolie I judged from his appearance) willingly submitted themselves to the mellowing influence of the brandy.

Next morning, 8 August, we got off at the surprisingly early hour of 9.30, accompanied by two camels carrying the baggage and a Mongolian horde to speed us on our way—the Amban himself, all the officers, and Sir Aurel Stein's coolie, whom I only recognised with difficulty, as he was now wearing a Homburg hat, silver-rimmed sun goggles, and knickerbockers, looking like a great explorer in his own right. At the first village the cavalcade dismounted and after a long bout of grinning and handshaking the Lesser Horde took its departure and we headed for the north.

At this point the Tashkurghan river is deflected eastwards and a low ridge, pierced by the narrow gorge of the Tagharma river, separates its wide valley from the even more extensive Tagharma plain. This extends to the north for about twelve miles, until it meets another ridge upon which lies the Ulugh Rabat pass (14,000 ft.). The pass leads into another almost equally wide valley running north between the Sarikol range on the west and the Muztagh Ata and Kungur groups to the east. The Tagharma plain abounds in villages and cultivation, while the higher valley beyond is the happy home of many Kirghiz, their herds and their flocks.

Emerging from the bare yellow rock gorge we were delighted by the sight of the green Tagharma vale, its scattered villages, the tall poplars, the browsing herds, and waving wheat-fields. Our guides, vaguely aware that the consular mind was intent on mountains, took us too far to the east in the direction of the most southerly foothills of the Muztagh Ata group, until we finally came to rest in a village at the foot of a nallah, which undoubtedly led directly to the heart of the mountains. With some difficulty we resisted the insistent invitation of this interesting unknown nallah, and next morning we sheered away to the north-west in the direction of the Ulugh Rabat pass. The transport—ponies now instead of camels—passed us going at the rate of knots and Naiad Shah was instructed to tell the men to halt for the night at a grazing ground this side of the pass. But he apparently failed to select from his repertoire the correct language in which to give the order, for

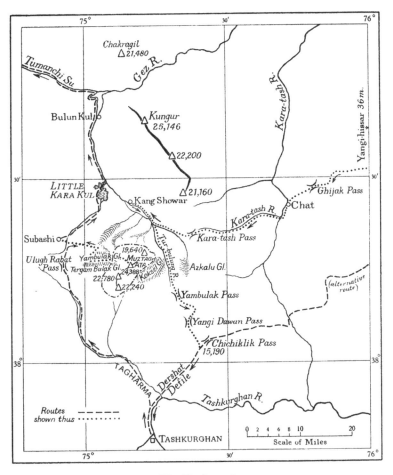

Map 5: The Kashgar Journey

when we reached the place—all of us fully ripe for stopping—there was no sign of the ponies. Shipton, the two mounted infantrymen whom we had been obliged to accept as escort, and anyone else whose beast was capable of it, galloped off in pursuit but without success. By 7 p.m. we were on top of the Ulugh Rabat and in extremely bad tempers. There was a noble prospect to the dark plain below and the white dome of Muztagh Ata above, now rapidly dissolving in the dusk. But the noblest prospect is improved by the sight of an inn, and though our inn was now in sight on the plain below, it was rapidly receding across it. How we reviled that man of many tongues. Water arrested the march of the flying column and by 8 p.m. we and our transport were united by some muddy pools. Stragglers were still coming in an hour later. Most high uplands are made unpleasant by constant wind, but that night we were spared the usual gale which makes cooking in the open impossible. While supper was preparing we had leisure to reflect on the truth of Cromwell's remark that 'no man goes further than he who does not know where he is going'.

We were now fairly under the western slopes of Muztagh Ata, and although we were not yet within striking distance we were well able to appreciate its enormous bulk. The south side of this so-called 'Father of Ice Mountains' is defended by two outlying peaks each over 22,000 ft.; the north side is steep and broken and the east side is unexplored. (On my return journey I passed round by the east side, but bad weather shut out any view of the mountain.) The west side is a huge gently curving sweep of snow, the lower part split by three almost parallel glaciers. Originating at about 20,000 ft. in deep narrow clefts these glaciers, when they reach the snow line at about 17,000 ft., spill and spread over the slopes of brown scree like streams of white lava, descending in a cascade of ice pinnacles to as low as 14,000 ft. That one aspect alone of a mountain can contain three such glaciers is an indication of its breadth, for the lower parts of the glaciers are separated by two or even three miles of scree slope.

Two names famous in Central Asian exploration are connected with Muztagh Ata. In 1894 the great Swedish explorer Sven Hedin, in addition to making a rough survey of the mountain, made four attempts to climb it. Rough survey is the word, for he ascribed to it a height of 25,600 ft., and 'the unchallenged pre-eminence over the peaks which cluster round, which is proved by its name "Father of Ice Mountains"'. The Kungur group, less than twenty-five miles north-east, he either ignored or else did not see, for the unaided eye can appreciate that one at least of its peaks is higher than Muztagh Ata. As for the name, the story is that the reply to the question about its name was simply 'Muztagh, Ata' or 'Ice Mountain, O Father'. In 1900 the late Sir Aurel Stein made a survey of the Sarikol valley and his sur-veyor, Ram Singh of the Indian Survey, carried out the triangulation of the Muztagh Ata and Kungur groups, discovering that the highest peak of Kungur is 25,146 ft. against 24,388 ft. for Muztagh Ata.

Having studied both the ground and Sven Hedin's account of his attempts we decided that the best line of approach was that between the two largest of these western glaciers, the Yam Bulak and the Tergam Bulak. Some Kirghiz yorts were reported to be in a valley north of the Yam Bulak glacier about two hours away and there we thought we would have our base.

In these parts of Sinkiang yorts exert a powerful attraction which the wise traveller should on no account resist. Such a thought never occurred to us for a moment—we merely crawled from one yort to the next, drinking tea, eating yoghourt, and studying nomadic life, though we ourselves were much more nomadic than our hosts, whose lives seemed to be remarkably static, even sedentary. Since travellers are rare they are usually welcome; food, fire, and shelter are automati-cally put at their disposal by the kindly Kirghiz.

When we reached the little valley under the slopes of the moun-tain where we had proposed harbouring, we were disturbed to find only one yort. All the families but one had just moved down to Sub-ashi a few miles away and the principal place of the Sarikol plain. The remaining one, too, was about to go but they readily postponed their departure when they heard that Mrs Shipton would be alone for a few days while we were on the mountain. In the afternoon we sorted out food for our expedition and in the evening we walked up towards the Yam Bulak glacier to reconnoitre a route for the morrow. On the moraine two herds of what looked like wild goats were playing about.

Sven Hedin was a great explorer, but he made no claim to be a mountaineer. As he therefore had no false pride to maintain he made full use of the local aids to progress in his attempts on the mountain.

Of the four his most successful was the second, when, carried on the back of a yak, he claimed to have reached a height of 20,600 ft. As he justly observes, the secret of freedom from the troubles of altitude (a secret which so far has eluded research) 'is the avoidance of bodily exertion'.

He employed yaks for all his attempts and from his free use of them on the mountain we may deduce several things; the absence of any technical difficulties on the west side, at any rate for a great part of the way up; the absence of man-power in Sinkiang, where no Turki who can afford an ass and no Kirghiz who owns a yak or a pony ever walks, much less carries anything; and finally the all-round supremacy of yaks over donkeys, mules, horses, camels, or even elephants, though Hannibal might dispute the last. As a load-carrier the yak's powers are well known, but his virtues as a hack are unrecognised. Although Central Asia is the ancestral home of the horse, one may travel there a long time without becoming aware of it, or if already aware of it one may conclude that he has remained at home too long. No doubt there are some good horses, but the locals very wisely keep them for themselves, mounting the innocent stranger on their sorriest screws, so that if it should happen to fall down with him no harm is done except, perhaps, to the stranger.

A good riding yak is much to be preferred to the sort of beast one is commonly invited to put one's leg over. He will do his three miles an hour without the incessant kicking and flogging which is essential in keeping the local jade up to the bit (the yak, by the way, has no bit, only a rope through the nose), while his short legs and quick step give the rider the comfortable if illusory impression that he is covering the ground at a great rate. On going uphill there is no need for the rider to dismount to spare his yak. On going downhill there is no need for him to dismount to spare his own neck, for the yak takes everything as it comes, uphill or downhill, rough or smooth. In fording rivers, despite those short legs, he is as steady as a rock, for his great weight keeps him well anchored to the bottom. And, of course, at heights of 16,000 ft. or more, when the horse like the rest of us is beginning to suffer from the effects of height, the yak is just beginning to feel at home; he may blow like a grampus but his tremendous girth ensures that there is plenty of air in the bellows. And finally, if the snow is reached, he is sent ahead to break a trail for the floundering men and horses behind him; and should his fortunate rider need a pair of sun glasses all he has to do is to turn round and yank a length of hair from his copious tail.*

Profiting by Sven Hedin's example Shipton and I determined that though we ourselves might condescend to walk we should have a yak to carry our camp to the snow-line at about 17,000 ft. Not wishing to retract much of what I have just written I must assume that our yak was the exception that proves the rule, or that like all other mountaineers yaks have their off days. He was, indeed, a total failure.

With stores for six days the three of us started on 11 August accompanied by a Sherpa (Gyalgen, a former Everest porter and one of Shipton's servants), a Turki lad, a yak and his driver. The weather since we left Tashkurghan had been cloudy and unsettled, but this day was fine, calm, and sunny. Having rounded the snout of the Yam Bulak glacier, three or four miles from the yort, we took the long easy scree slope lying between that glacier and the Tergam Bulak to the south of it. Unencumbered ourselves, confident in our yak's prowess, we climbed comfortably to about 16,000 ft., where we sat down to await the arrival of the yak and the rest of the party. Time passed, our confidence waned. Nothing could be heard, nothing seen, for the slope, from bottom almost to top, being as convexly regular as a schoolroom globe, limited our horizon to less than a hundred yards. Reluctantly we started down to investigate and presently came upon Gyalgen, the Turki, and the yak driver, staggering up under heavy loads. Of the yak, the party's main hope and king-pin, there was no sign. He had very sensibly struck and sat down at the very first hint of what was expected of him. The driver, too, thought no more of mountaineering than did his charge. Groaning and moaning on account of his splitting headache, and fearful of the certain death that awaited us if we proceeded, he had to be sent down at once, pursued by sounds of desultory illwill. The rest of us struggled on with the loads, marvelling how much better they did these things in Sven Hedin's time.

Shipton, discarding chivalry in favour of the principle of economy of force, had allowed his wife to relieve him of a sleeping-bag and a

---

* A few black hairs stretched across the eyes, while allowing one to see, are semi-effective against glare.

cork mattress. There was apparently more in marriage than I had yet realised, but now it was too late to repair the omission and I had to bear my own burden. We plodded on for another thousand feet and camped at 3 p.m. just below the first snow at about 17,000 ft. From here Mrs Shipton and the Turki lad went down, leaving Gyalgen, myself, and her grateful but unfeeling husband to finish the job.

That evening we did a short reconnaissance. Just above our tent, scree gave place to snow, or rather ice, for the snow had melted from the lowest 200 or 300 ft. of underlying ice. The slope, however, was gentle, so that with care one could walk without nicking steps. Higher up was a short ice-fall which could be turned, beyond that a long stretch of crevassed snow-slope, and beyond that again unbroken slopes extending to the summit dome. Most of this, except for the actual summit whose exact whereabouts we could not locate, we had already seen from below. Our safe and methodical plan was to have a camp at about 20,000 ft. and another at 22,000 ft. from which no matter how moderately we rated ourselves, we ought to have no great difficulty in crawling to the top.

Next day we started, Shipton and I carrying very modest loads and Gyalgen rather an immodest one. The ice-fall was soon overcome by an outflanking movement, and having threaded our way through the worst of the crevassed section we camped at 3 p.m. in a snow hollow, crediting ourselves with a rise of 3000 ft. The snow was in really excellent condition, everything was going to be too easy. This gratuitous supposition and Gyalgen's faltering under his too heavy load had already caused an alteration in a perfectly sound plan. Assuming that the snow, so good here, could be no worse higher up and might well be better, we agreed to cut out the intermediate camp at 22,000 ft. and to take only one bite at the cherry—an agreement which I, aware of my advancing years and limited high-climbing powers, had no right to make. We arrived at this pregnant decision during a halt on the way up from Camp 1, while we were pondering over ways of easing Gyalgen's burden, neither of us having the indelicacy to suggest taking some of it upon ourselves. Since this new plan meant that we should, if all went well, spend only one more night on the mountain some of the food (we had four days' supply) could be dumped. But Shipton's liberal ideas of dumping and his ruthless whittling down to a bare one day's

supply led to a sharp debate. Although I may have had private misgivings about our only needing one day's food I had already agreed to the
change of plan and there was little I could urge against this wholesale
sacrifice beyond the desirability of keeping an ample reserve. Possibly the fact that nothing from my own load was dumped made me the
more reluctant to see so much left behind.

As I had been on Rakaposhi only two months before, I expected
to be better acclimatised than I proved to be; but there, though we had
been twice to 20,000 ft. we had never slept higher than 17,000 ft. That
night I had a violent headache and in the morning felt no more like
climbing four feet than the four thousand odd which we had cheerfully
set ourselves. Still it had to be done—one day being our self-allotted
span—so at 6 a.m. we got under way.

Though not a breath of wind stirred in our hollow, it was notice-
ably cold in the bleak and pallid dawn. Merely by fumbling with buttons after some necessary business outside my thumbs and forefingers
were so chilled that they never felt right for the rest of the day. Well
down as we were on the west side of this considerable protuberance
on the earth's sphere—almost another sphere in itself—the sun would
be long in reaching us. The more reason therefore for pressing rapidly
onwards and upwards to meet it, so off we went over the good hard
snow. For a thousand feet we climbed rapidly and hopefully, and then
conditions suddenly became worse. The snow assumed that vile consistency which necessitates one's stamping with all one's might once,
twice, or even three times to ensure that the step will not give way the
moment it is stood upon. Worse still, a wind started to blow. Its force
seemed negligible—in the unlikely event of our wearing straw hats I
doubt if we should have had to hold them on—but nevertheless it cut
to the bone. The exertion of stamping steps contributed nothing to our
warmth, nor did the sun when it at length reached us, so that even at
this early stage the effects of these conditions became serious. Shipton
was overcome by a fit of rigor and lay shaking in the snow, while we sat
by shivering with a violence only a little less.

On we plodded up that vast tilted snow-field, seeing no other
mountains either to north or south by which to measure our progress.
Though we moved slowly we moved continuously, for it was too cold
to sit and rest and eat. As early as 1 o'clock we had the impression of

arriving somewhere, but two hours later all we could say was that that impression was no weaker. Still we thought the end must be very near. We reckoned we had climbed a thousand feet in the first hour when the snow was good, and having been climbing steadily since then for eight hours we argued that most of the remaining three thousand odd feet were below us. Whenever we dared to look up our eyes met the same unbroken snow horizon, maintaining its unconquerably rigid distance of two or three hundred feet. And now the long hours of cold, fatigue, and deferred hope began to tell.

Some while before this my contribution to step-kicking had become of small account and presently Gyalgen, too, found himself unable to take his turn. Shipton had still a little left in him, so that we agreed to struggle on for another half-hour until 3.30 p.m. when, if there was still no firm indication of the summit, we would give up and try again another day. Quite early in the afternoon I had suggested going back so that next day we should have the advantage of a great many ready-made steps; but this had been overruled on the grounds that tomorrow the steps might no longer be there. This was true enough because, when we did come to go down, we had trouble even to find the steps, so completely had the driving snow filled them.

After a generous half-hour's extra play in this hard-fought game between the mountain and ourselves a decision in our favour seemed as far off as ever. For me the delusion of the summit being at hand had long become stale, stimulating despair rather than hope. I feared that even if we reached a point from which the summit could be seen we should find it at the wrong end of a long flat ridge, for the perversity of inanimate objects is always a factor to be reckoned with. By this time we were all pretty well on our knees. Had the summit been in sight and our remaining task measurable, some hidden reserves of strength might have been found, but there was still nothing to be seen beyond the next hundred feet or so of snow. To persevere one must have hope, and this, which had been pretty severely tried, had now perished, worn out by too long deferment.

If we allowed only two hours to get down there was still time enough to struggle on for another hour could we but force our bodies onwards. But before the clock had time to impose its decision on us we gave up. Perhaps we were weak-minded—in fact, we damned ourselves

On the Kukuay col (*c.* 19,000 ft.)—the Batura glacier
is below to the left

View down the Kukuay glacier from the col

Hunza gorge scenery

heartily later—but our wisest actions are sometimes those for which we are not fully responsible and the sequel showed that we did well to go down. Exclusive of halts for vomiting by Shipton the descent did take about two hours. Our up-coming tracks were by now obliterated, so that the finding of the way through the crevassed area was less easy than it had before been. After dark we could not have found it.

Back in the tent an unpleasant discovery awaited us. All the toes on one of Shipton's feet were frost-bitten. They were dead white that evening and black the next morning. The tips of both my big toes were slightly touched and went black, but came painfully back to life forty-eight hours later. I was wearing the 'expedition' boots with the heavy moulded rubber soles and Shipton a pair of the heavily nailed porters' boots which I had brought out for Rakaposhi and which he maintained had got wet the previous day so that they had ice inside them before we started. Gyalgen, who was wearing lightly nailed boots, came to no harm. As a purely speculative consolation it may not amount to much, but there is little doubt that had we persevered for another hour the damage would have been much more serious. Success would have been a very considerable consolation, but it would only have been gained at a high cost. Failure with frost-bite thrown in was a tough bullet to chew.

The condition of Shipton's foot was, of course, decisive—we had to go down—but in point of fact not one of us was fit to try again next day or even for several days. The effort had taken more out of us than we realised and a week later I still found it more than usually trying to walk uphill at all.

Whether the top of the mountain is a long flat ridge or whether, as seems more likely, it is a flattish dome we still do not know. Shipton is of the opinion that we were on the summit dome and not more than a hundred feet below the top. An inexcusable assumption of the probable snow conditions, over-confidence in our powers, and the unexpected cold, had proved our undoing, and of these, only of the last had we any right to complain. In early June on the North Col of Everest one would not experience such cold. Here it was mid-August, and though Muztagh Ata is in Lat. 38° and Everest is 10° further south one would not expect that to make so much difference. We live and learn, and big mountains are stern teachers.

CHAPTER XII

TO KASHGAR

———◆———

CUSTOM ORDAINED and self-respect demanded that in the morning we should talk of taking the camp higher. Nevertheless, having packed up, we turned our backs to the mountain and went down, finding that not altogether easy. We reached the foot at 1 p.m. where we dumped the loads and hobbled dejectedly back to the yort. My toes were beginning to tingle, Shipton's were numb and blistered. The Kirghiz had their own remedy for frostbite—a nasty mixture of soot and butter—but there was really nothing to be done except to apply clean dressings, get back to Kashgar, and await the event.

We moved down to Subashi, where there is a considerable 'aoul' (a village of yorts) and also a Chinese post. Kirghiz and Chinese both contended for the possession of the bodies, so that before we escaped to a large and cleanly yort we were obliged to drink tea and lunch with both. From there we loitered onwards across this pleasant plain, past browsing camels and yaks, while ahead of us towered the great Kungur ridge with its glaciers tumbling down to the plain like so many waterfalls. In due course we came to the Little Kara Kul—a sapphire gem set in green and gold—and camped by its quiet waters, now gently ruffled by the wind, now calmly reflecting that 'sunny pleasure-dome with caves of ice' from which we had so recently been turned away.

Little Kara Kul is a fine sheet of water, but it is less than half the size of the better known Great Kara Kul over on the Russian side of the Sarikol range which is some twelve miles in length. Little Kara Kul is a lake formed by a moraine of one of the Kungur glaciers of a former era. It drains to the north to the Bulun Kul by a passage cut through the moraine.

Bulun Kul, which was our next stage, lies in one of the windiest defiles imaginable, comparable as a natural wind-tunnel to the Jikyop gorge through which one passes on the way to Everest. The rocky western slopes of the defile are covered for several hundred feet up by great sand dunes, which from a distance we mistook for snow. The ferocious blast which met us explained how the sand had got up there, but we did not solve the puzzle of where it had come from until next day when the track led us for several miles over a dry lake bed of salt encrusted sand.

At Bulun Kul there was the usual squalid dreary police post with its equally squalid garrison. This seemed more apathetic and miserable than the usual run of garrisons, for its commander had died the previous day as the result of a bursting rifle. The bolt had blown back and penetrated the forehead. A messenger had brought a confused account of this accident to us at Subashi where he had come to ask Mrs Shipton for some medicine suitable for a man with a headache. Some headache! A few days before she had had to treat a Kirghiz with half his fingers blown off and his face mottled with powder blast as the result of a similar accident. 'Ah me, what perils do environ, the man who meddles with cold iron'—especially when it is old and of unreliable make. This explains, I think, why our escort was so loth to take potshots at geese or duck when the chance offered. They said that ammunition was scarce and strictly checked, but I should think the fear of a bursting rifle was the chief deterrent.

Either the searching and incessant wind of Bulun Kul, or maybe the Chinese garrison, had stripped the local Kirghiz of most of their wealth and with it had gone their hospitable nature. Having taken shelter from the blast in a dirty and draughty yort where we crouched by a feeble fire for an hour without the offer of a drop of milk or a spoonful of yoghourt, we slunk away to our tents only to have them presently levelled to the ground by gusts of gale force.

By morning the wind had dropped and we cantered happily away from that sandy seat of misery across the wide salt plain. The river meanders through this dry lake-bed until at the north end it plunges suddenly into the Gez defile. This is the shortest road to Kashgar, but in summer when the rivers are up it is not possible to go through with animals. We therefore turned left-handed up the Tumanchi Su, another glorious vale, dotted with 'aouls' and fat with great flocks of sheep and herds of yaks and camels. Anxious to give the Kirghiz the opportunity of retrieving their good name and to erase the bitter memories of the night we repaired to the nearest yort. We were not disappointed. Having drunk tea, we lay on rugs, ladling in yoghourt, and gazing through the open door across the plain to the two splendid 22,000 ft. peaks of Chakragil on the north side of the Gez defile. With mingled pleasure and mortification, for these peaks were to have been our objective after Muztagh Ata, we followed our route to the top and in imagination saw below us the pine-clad valleys of the eastern slopes. It is one of the curiosities of Kashgaria that whereas on the Sarikol side of these Chakragil mountains not a stick grows, the eastern valleys are heavily timbered.

Our next day's march up the narrowing Tumanchi Su valley was the most unashamed yort crawl we had so far achieved. A short half-hour after starting we were climbing unreluctantly from our mounts by the smart whitey-grey, opulent-looking yort of the local 'Beg'—the 'big shot' as I very wittily used to call these wealthy patriarchs. Tea, bread, and cream were put before us—such cream as was not to be drowned in tea, nor was any bread required to assist in the swallowing of large quantities of it. The tea that is drunk in the course of a persevering and extended yort crawl such as ours, not to mention that which is drunk in camp, is as varied in colour, constitution, and taste as the bottled pain-killers on a chemist's shelves. The only common factor is that none of it much resembles tea. It may be hot water stained by the tea-pot, hot water in which the loess haze has settled, hot milk into which a used tea-leaf has inadvertently strayed, hot milk with an infusion of willow bark, hot water with a dash of curry powder, or merely very badly made tea. The usual ingredient for making tea, it will be gathered, is scarce among the Kirghiz so that it is wise to travel with half a sack of cheap tea—a mixture of tea dust and loess dust—and to confer the doubtful blessing of a double handful of it in return for any benefits received.

We pulled up at our fifth and last group of yorts early in the after-noon, though at the head of the valley there were two more 'aouls' in sight which the purists of the party thought ought not to have been neglected. However, the cup of pleasure should not be drained at one gulp. We should have to pass them to-morrow, and to-day we had much to arrange, for the next march included, or should have included, the crossing of the Ulugh Art—a pass of 16,600 ft.—and our final departure from the friendly Kirghiz of Sarikol. Sven Hedin had crossed this pass in the reverse direction and on the descent to this side had had his horse killed by a fall; he devotes several pages to a description of it and calls it 'a perilous pass, the worst I have ever crossed in any part of Asia'.

The Leh-Yarkand trade route over the Karakoram crosses several high passes, two of which are over 18,000 ft., and although horses are the principal means of transport their mortality is dreadful. For high passes the yak is much to be preferred, but here, we were told, none was available. To our inexpert eyes there seemed to be quite a few suitable yaks grunting about, but these were either in calf or in milk so that when we started we had, in addition to Shipton's black horse (on loan) and Mrs Shipton's languid chestnut mare, five ponies and three donkeys. We were aware we should have a long day, but no one could tell us how long. On the usual routes the accepted measure for distance is the 'pao t'ai', the Chinese 'milestone' which is actually about two-and-a-half miles, but the impossibility of getting a rough estimate of distance or even of time from a Kirghiz or a Turki is extraordinary. 'Very far' or 'near' is as much as they will commit themselves to, which may mean anything from one to fifty miles. A bow-shot or a biscuit-toss, even in the absence of bows or biscuits, are fairly definite ideas, but in Sinkiang a 'day's march' conveys no more information than a 'day's run' in a car where much depends on the car and the driver's ideas. A man alone riding a horse with his baggage under him may do fifty miles in a day, while a string of baggage ponies will not do much more than twenty. Nor could the pony men tell us anything about the route which they must have known well enough—whether there was anywhere to camp this side of the pass, or whether, once committed, it was a case of all or nothing. To make things more difficult, our linguist Naiad Shah had retired to Tashkurghan, his stock having slumped since the Ulugh Rabat episode, and Gyalgen's Turki, though fluent, seemed lacking in precision.

Having crossed a low ridge, whence we had a view of Kaufmann Peak* (23,000 ft.) a hundred miles away west of the Great Kara Kul, we found ourselves in the wide stony bed of the Ulugh Art river. The water had all disappeared under the stones to emerge lower down and there was no grass to refresh the animals during the midday halt. In the afternoon, as we climbed the slopes on the north side of the valley, we

---

* Now called 'Lenin Peak'.

passed a 'gumbaz' and a bit of grass, but we were so intent on the pass that no one suggested that we should spend the night there. The crossing of two glacier streams cost us some delay, the path became rougher, and four miniature passes intervened, so that it was not until six o'clock that we stood at the foot of the pass itself, regarding with dismay the track zig-zagging steeply upwards for nearly a thousand feet. To be confronted by this at the end of a long hungry march was too much, but we could not stay where we were. On our right lay the ice-stream of the Ulugh glacier, descending from insignificant hills of 17,000 ft. and surprising us by its size, while on our left great cliffs of green and purple rock looked like the scene of a mountaineer's nightmare. A grey glacier pool, in which small icebergs jostled, offered us water, but not a blade of grass, a stick of wood, or a handful of dry dung were to be had. There was nothing for it but to go on. But when we in front had got about half-way up we began to have serious doubts about our transport. Every few steps horses and donkeys were stopping and it was only with increasing difficulty that they were urged on again. It would be dark before they were up. None of us knew how bad the descent might be, so we turned tail and spent a cold hungry night by the glacier pool. The animals ate nothing whatever, for though we offered half a sack of rice none of the drivers would consider giving it to their beasts.

However reliable the transport and easy the road there is often reason to regret having left the baggage train to fend for itself. To get separated from one's baggage is a mistake usually avoidable, often committed, and always regretted. On this occasion it was, I think, the biting cold of the early morning which persuaded the three of us to push on ahead of our transport. We climbed the pass before eight o'clock, sat on its broad gravel summit until driven off by a cruel wind, and then descended a thousand feet by an equally steep rough path. When last seen the transport had just started up the lower slopes. We sat with our eyes glued to the pass playing at 'Sister Anne'. By eleven o'clock the only signs of life we had seen were some figures which mysteriously appeared and disappeared by the summit cairn. Had the caravan been attacked by bandits and were these their scouts watching us? It seemed a far-fetched explanation, but we could think of nothing better which might account for their taking four hours to climb a thousand feet.

With disgraceful slowness—the after-effects of Muztagh Ata—I climbed back to the cairn, taking the fanciful precaution of not approaching it directly from the path. There was no one there, but some of the baggage lay piled. On the other side I met Gyalgen and two Kirghiz lads carrying up loads, driving the three donkeys and the unladen chestnut mare, Lydia Languish, in front of them. The disaster had been pretty complete and these were the sole remnants of our caravan. Shipton's black horse had dropped dead soon after starting, breaking the stock of his gun as it fell, and the Kirghiz had taken back their three sick and sorry animals lest they too should follow his untimely example. Lydia Languish was too exhausted to carry anything, but the gallant little donkeys still had their loads. In the course of the afternoon we collected everything by a wretchedly inadequate patch of grass at the foot of the pass. The last to come in was a Turki lad bearing the skin of the black horse which he was taking back to Kashgar to satisfy his master that the horse was in fact dead and had not been sold or lost.

Next day with everyone carrying a load or a parcel of some sort we made about seven miles down a vile barren valley where even a yak or a camel would have been hard put to it to find nourishment. Gyalgen disappeared up a side nallah to some yorts to get help, and returned the following morning alone driving six yaks and eight calves. The owners, who no doubt mistook him for a Chinese soldier, were too frightened either to stop him or to come with him. Before he got back we had had a scene with the two Kirghiz boys who had first tried to bolt and then wept, but upon the arrival of the yaks they cheered up and helped to load them. In Northern Tibet there are wild yaks and I think we can claim to have discovered that they exist also in Sinkiang. These behaved like wild steers. Each in turn bucked its load off and then galloped grunting up the nallah. Finally, we started with two of the more placid, followed by four woolly calves and our three donkeys which were still strong enough to carry though this was their third day without a proper feed. That morning we had made large numbers of chapattis for them.

That evening our transport troubles were solved, for we reached a small Turki village at the foot of the valley where we managed to hire two camels for the long stretch of desert to Opal Bazaar. Here was grass in abundance, but almost before the wretched donkeys had got used to the sight of it they were whisked away by the two Kirghiz boys who hurried off up the valley without even waiting to be paid. In order to make an early start the next morning the camels were brought to our camp and tethered for the night. Our precaution was in some ways unfortunate, for one of them proceeded to make night hideous by roaring for her calf left behind in the village. A camel mourning for its young makes a noise very like a fog-horn blown at regular intervals.

At the mouth of the valley the river loses itself beneath its stony mile-wide bed not to reappear again until near Opal, the intervening tract of thirty miles being a sand and gravel plain utterly devoid of water or life. Opal is a large fertile village situated some thirty miles west of Kashgar on a plateau of rich loess soil. To an observer on the desert it appears as if it were placed upon a hill and its groves of tall poplars so strengthen the illusion that one wonders how water reached it at all. On entering the oasis one has the impression of landing on a tropical island* after a long sea voyage, so bewilderingly sudden is the transition from dreary waste to rich fields of lucerne, maize, and melons, and brimming channels of brick-red water. We were all very tired, but although the bazaar was five miles further on we straggled towards it against an outflowing tide of donkeys, stopping often by the way to eat melons from the fields. Long after dark we reached the noisy, thronging, lamplit bazaar. The house of the 'big shot' which we automatically sought was deserted, but we soon had our legs under a table in the house of his deputy. Having eaten as much bread, melon, and grapes, as we could well hold, not without some grumbling at the lean fare, we went to bed and at midnight were awakened to eat the dinner for which these were but the *hors d'oeuvre*.

A messenger, we were assured, who would ride like the wind, had been dispatched almost as soon as we arrived, so that we fully expected a lorry to come for us next morning. We sat all that day in the high, bare, mosque-like room, brushing off flies and visitors, while each successive meal betrayed a fall in the standard of living. That fish and guests stink after three days and must be thrown out was evidently a

---

*   The Chinese for oasis is 'lu chow' – green island.

saying not unknown to our host who seemed preparing to act on it betimes. Towards midnight the truck arrived, and we learnt that the swift, hard-riding messenger had left that morning at seven o'clock on a donkey.

Opal is like a reef thrown out from the great Kashgar oasis—a few short desert inroads are crossed and soon forgotten when one enters what appears to be one vast garden stretching unbroken in every direction, lavishly watered and carefully tended. Kashgar is, perhaps, the largest of a string of great oases which lie round the periphery of the Takla Makan desert. The simplest way of grasping the geography of Sinkiang as a whole is to think in terms of desert, oasis, mountain. The heart and by the far the largest part of the country is the Takla Makan desert itself, 600 miles long from east to west and 300 miles across. Except for the narrower eastern end which forms the Kansu corridor— the link between China and its westernmost province—this desert is surrounded by snow mountains which are also roughly the boundaries of Sinkiang. On the north are the Tien Shan; to the west Chakragil, Kungur, Muztagh Ata, and Sarikol; and to the south the Karakoram and the Kun Lun. Between snow mountains and desert lies this comparatively narrow strip of rich land, which owes its fertility entirely to the many rivers which hurry through it in the course of their short life from their birthplace among the high snows and glaciers to their death and burial in the thirsty desert. No river ever leaves Sinkiang.

In the middle of Kashgar, like a quiet inner oasis, is the British Consulate where within the high walls of the compound there broods a Sabbath calm, free from the rude turmoil of the city. In a place whose motor vehicles could be counted on one hand one might think that turmoil would be far to seek, or that the easy-going medieval way of life in Kashgar would be incapable of creating much stir; but when a sufficiency of Turkis, their asses, their oxen, their camels, their men-servants and their maid-servants, gather together on a market day it is surprising how like it can be to Oxford Street during the New Year Sales. True it is that there are a lot of flies, that the street is littered with melon rind instead of bus tickets, that the equally dense traffic consists mainly of donkeys, and that the smell is something other but no more offensive than that of petrol fumes, but there is the same sense of infectious haste and false urgency.

Bazaars and markets are always interesting and sometimes attractive, especially if one has a profound admiration for food in the raw and in vast quantity, and here in Kashgar the narrow streets are every day adorned with the same horticultural splendour as the inside of a church at a Harvest Festival. If bread is the staff of life, to the Turkoman melons are life itself, and here they are in prodigious quantity and variety—green and golden spheres, sliced half-moons of cream and scarlet—major planets among a galaxy of peaches, nectarines, apricots, rosy deceitful pomegranates, and white and purple grapes. Against this rich back-cloth are set piles of more homely massive onions, mountains of grated onion, stately leeks, radishes as big as turnips, pyramids of eggs, hills of rice, and towers of bread. There was really little else but food, raw and cooked, to be seen. The odd junk shop seemed to apologise for its unbeautiful, unwanted presence; no jeweller's wares challenged the coruscating fruit; no craftsmen plied their trade save in the obscurity of a back street where they could not impede the great business of life, the buying, selling, and eating of so much wholesome 'belly-timber'. A delightful scene, even to a stern ascetic moralist; for who, having seen even once the full tide of life in Kashgar bazaar, would not feel his confidence in the human race restored, or would not, in the words of the hymn, fail to 'ponder anew what the Almighty can do' even with a people not remarkable for diligence.

I visited this stirring scene but once and even then I hurried through very early in the day while there was still room to squeeze between the donkeys without being beaten to the ground by their maunds of melons. Nor, with one exception, did I visit any shrines, mosques, Chinese temples, or celebrated antiquities, where I could presumably count on being alone. The exception was a climbing archaeological expedition to what Sir Aurel Stein calls the 'Och Mirwan'—three caves or 'cellas' with the painted head of a Buddha, carved out of a solid cliff of loess situated in the bed of the Artush river two miles beyond the northern end of the Kashgar oasis. The caves were half-way up, or down, the 100 ft. high vertical cliff, so that to reach them it was necessary to 'abseil' down with the rope anchored to a wooden stake driven into the top of the cliff; then to affect a lodgement in the cave by drawing oneself in with the feet; and, having satisfied one's archaeological lust, to continue the 'abseil' to the bottom. As

Shipton was *hors de combat* I was the victim required to make a Roman holiday for a small party of visitors we had brought out to watch proceedings from below. Although my grace and agility may not have impressed them, I feel sure that the possibilities of the situation did. I was amazed by the extraordinary preservation of this relic of a distant age carved in such a seemingly insubstantial medium as a cliff of loess.

This, I'm afraid, was the sum of our meagre tribute laid on the altar of learning. As Dr Johnson says: 'if love of ease surmounted our desire for knowledge, the offence has not the invidiousness of singularity', and so pleasant was it at Chini Bagh, the Consulate, dissecting melons, critically fingering peaches, and thinking of the busy world outside that it was distasteful to sally out even in response to calls of hospitality.

In Kashgar the Consul must undertake the duties which hospitality requires with all seriousness, so that anyone staying at the Consulate is drawn willy-nilly into the whirlpool. My first call—Shipton on crutches was absolved—was to the Russian Consulate for lunch. The Consul was a pleasant man with an original sense of humour, which, I should think, most Russian officials must develop, even if unconsciously. The English-speaking interpreter was a flaxen-haired, pink and white young man, but even with his willing assistance I did not penetrate very far behind the Iron Curtain. I made a point of asking about this piece of stage furniture and was chagrined to find that neither of them had the slightest idea what it meant or what it implied.

The Russian and British Consulates in Kashgar—the only two of the kind—are like the ends of a see-saw, each has its ups and downs. From 1934 to 1942 the Russians were up. They had everything their own way and the Chinese Governor in their pocket, but in 1942 when they were in serious difficulties the Chinese reasserted themselves. Since then the Russian end of the see-saw has stayed down, much to our advantage. Although communications with Russia as compared with India are short and easy, all traffic, whether goods or mail, is at present (1948) suspended. As the Consul lugubriously explained to me, after sitting secluded for three months doing nothing beyond maintaining correct but distant relations with the Chinese, he spends a day or two of activity making up and dispatching the consular mail and then relapses into hibernation until the next Quarter Day. Having in accordance with tradition consumed a sufficiency of brandy, vodka, and champagne, I stumbled from behind the Iron Curtain not much wiser than before.

My next duty was to attend the Chinese celebration of 'V.J. Day' held on an open field near the New City six miles east of Old Kashgar. The Chinese as colonists of the 'New Dominion', as it is called, keep even more to themselves than do we in our tropical colonies though, perhaps, with less reason. They are not content to segregate themselves in one part of the town, but usually build a new settlement exclusively for themselves a few miles away. As they take little or no part in either business or in agriculture the Chinese population consists almost entirely of civil officials and the army. In spite of disasters and expulsions the Chinese have for many centuries clung tenaciously to their 'New Dominion'. This is all the more remarkable because of the enormous distance from China proper—a distance of 4000 miles. Even to-day travelling by lorry it is a matter of months rather than weeks. Since the first century B.C. Chinese power in Sinkiang has ebbed and flowed. Their last expulsion was in 1862 when the Dungans (Chinese Mahomedans) rebelled and drove them out. Yakub Beg, a man of great ability, whose government was recognised by both Britain and Russia, ruled in Kashgar until 1877 when a Chinese army recaptured their ancient dominion. The march of an army through 4000 miles of country upon which it was not possible to live, was accomplished by sending in advance troops who sowed cereals and vegetables in each oasis to be reaped in due course by the main body.

To drive through the Old City to the New in the consular truck was a moving experience for everyone. For none of the men, women, children, asses, or camels of these parts has any road sense (and why should they?) and assume, wrongly in this case, that the driver of a truck will either stop his vehicle or swerve out of the way, or that if he does not the resulting collision will be no more serious than that of two dawdling donkeys. It was refreshing to see such complete contempt for a mechanical vehicle, but one felt sorry for the victims.

The guests assembled on a raised pavilion, decorated with flags and the fly-blown portraits of the Allied leaders, to drink tea and eat melon seeds until all was ready. Opposite the pavilion were drawn up a long line of cavalry, some infantry who seemed to feel their lowly

At foot of Mintaka glacier

Mintaka glacier—the pass lies up
slope to left of pony

View across Mintaka glacier from pass
to peak on Hunza side

A glacier on Sinkiang side of Mintaka
pass

Rock peak near Beyik

Taghlak Gumbaz on bank of
Tashkurghan river

Moslem graves at Tashkurghan

Kirghiz boys with riding yak and
firelock at Kang Showar

position, some school-children, and a band. The ceremony consisted mainly of speeches in Chinese followed by a Turki translation and the repulsive shouting of slogans by the children and the troops in response to the ranting of a cheer-leader. The whole show was both amateurish and boring, and I inferred from the expression on the face of the Russian Consul, who arrived last in the uniform of a Bohemian admiral, that they did these things better in Moscow.

That night there was an official dinner on the grand scale which excited ripples of similar hospitality by officials of diminishing rank as though a stone had been cast into a quiet pond. Whether there were ten, twenty, or thirty courses at these banquets there was not as much variety as one would expect, for at least half of them were of meat served up in slightly different forms of vapidity. At Tashkurghan, some ten weeks' journey from the sea, our hosts had apologised for the absence of the usual delicacies, but here where it was only a matter of nine weeks there were the seaweeds and sea-fruits beloved of the Chinese—if sea-fruit is a permissible term for sea-slugs. The Chinese, like Peacock's Mr Jenkinson, though no anatomists, have concluded that man is omnivorous and on that conclusion they act.

From descriptions of Chinese feasts and from the competitive targets they set themselves in the number of courses, one might conclude that food played a paramount part. That is not so. Drinking is what is expected, particularly on the part of the guests, and this is done in the polite ceremonious fashion of the eighteenth and nineteenth centuries. There must be no quiet private sipping or swigging, but you must select your victim, raise your glass, and challenge him to 'bottoms up' for which the Chinese formula was what sounded to me like 'gambay'— at least if an ejaculation something similar to this is accompanied by the waving of your glass as you stand up your intentions are readily understood. Very rarely the chosen victim may not like your face or your manner, or more rarely still might think he had had enough, in which case the password is 'mambay' and there is then no obligation on either side to drain the glass. This formula should only be used in extremis, for a too frequent recurrence to it is considered bad form. The glasses were very small and contained, if one was lucky, nothing more deleterious than Russian brandy, so that even if one was struck by a salvo of 'gambays' after each course no great harm was done.

After one of these decorous orgies I was invited to the 'Russian Club' where a Chinese opera was being performed. The 'Club' is a fine large hall, holding possibly a thousand, with a big stage and its own lighting plant. It was put up by the Russians in the days when their influence was at its height. It is the only place of its kind in Kashgar and therefore the only place for any entertainment—the Russians occasionally show films, the Chinese use it for plays, operas, dancing, and meetings—so that it forms a constant and unmistakable piece of Russian propaganda.

Since I am an unenlightened yahoo in the matter of music and opera I am not qualified to write a criticism of the Chinese opera or music drama for which we arrived, most fortunately, only in time for the last act. Not that my ignorance of music or of Chinese would be any handicap, because of the first there was none, and as for the second whether an opera is sung in English, Chinese, or Italian, is all one to me so far as hearing and understanding goes. However, even I could comprehend the gestures and postures—not that they were indecent—and the grace of movement of even the lesser lights who took the parts of maids or messengers was fascinating to watch. The whole action took place round a sort of 'Punch and Judy' box stuck bang in the middle of the enormous stage. Behind it, where the puppets should have been, stood people who may have been prompters, stage managers, scene-shifters, or merely friends of the principals. Anyone, it appeared, was at liberty to stroll on from the wings to pass the time of day with the actors when they were not busy. The singing was the really excruciating part of the performance because it was all done in a high, forced falsetto, which the orchestra (o.p. side*) accompanied or not just as the spirit moved them, punctuating and emphasising the declamatory passages with gongs, cymbals, castanets, drums, and other percussion instruments at what each individual musician thought was an opportune moment. When the singing reached a pitch too high even for their accustomed ears they simply turned on the heat and extinguished it in a blast of cacophonous sound. A packed audience of Chinese soldiers and Turkis listened to all this in ominous silence with which I heartily agreed.

---

* 'Opposite Prompt' side: the offstage area to the right as one faces the audience—Ed

The stage was then cleared for a display of Turki dancing which was spirited and graceful but too long drawn out. As Swift says: 'there seems to be no part of knowledge in fewer hands than that of discerning when to have done.' This apparently was also the opinion of my Turki host, the Assistant Secretary. Inflamed to a moderate degree by the barrage of 'gambays' to which in his capacity of host he had been subjected, he felt that the shortest way of bringing the show to an end was to occupy the stage himself. Having lit a cigarette and donned a maroon coloured gown he mounted the stage and brought down the house with an admirable and not very unsteady display of grace and agility.

Three weeks soon passed, but it would be a mistake to suppose that they were passed in a round of banquets. Apart from those by which Mrs Shipton took her revenge there were only these few and a luncheon given by the Indian trading community. This, which was entirely devoted to simple but strenuous gastronomy, was more in my line—no drink, no idle chat, but a sustained and savage assault upon successive platters of pilau*, shirt-sleeves rolled up and towels round our necks.

For the most part I remained in the semi-monastic seclusion of Chini Bagh, walking in the garden and tasting the fruits thereof, and trying not to hear the daily argument between Shipton and another guest. The serpent in this garden was a journalist busy priming himself with the politics of Sinkiang with a view to unleashing them on an unsuspecting American public. Even with some striking examples of nourishment before him he was unable to disabuse his mind of the idea that the people of Kashgar were starving oppressed serfs; for instead of talking to the starving serfs at work on their bounteous crops, or getting himself crushed by a cart-load of melons in the teeming bazaar, he adopted at second or third hand the views of disgruntled politicians. He was distressed by the absence of any attempt to improve the Turki education, culture, or amenities—so different from the attention bestowed on such matters across the border—and he seemed not to agree with Mark Twain concerning the application of these things to the so-called backward races, that 'soap and education are not so

---

* The Chinese word for pilau is 'chua' – 'rice that is grabbed with the hand'.

sudden as a massacre but they are more deadly in the long run'. Like other progressive thinkers and fervid reformers—from our own bluff monster King Hal down to the disciples of Marx—he was not particular about the means used, but unlike them he was not really confident that the end was good. Such a fatal combination of views would not matter if unexpressed, but these roaming American journalists are well paid for their views even though these are sometimes half-baked. 'Does the wild ass bray when he hath grass?' was a question asked by Job, to which the answer seems to be that nowadays he very frequently does.

CHAPTER XIII

ANOTHER WAY HOME

N O CONSCIENTIOUS TRAVELLER turns homewards on the route by which he came if a reasonable alternative offers itself. I shall not try to define the saving word 'reasonable', but if this premise is granted then my curious choice of route for the return journey will be at least understood if not condoned.

Between Kashgar and Tashkurghan there are several routes to choose from: our own Ulugh Art route; the usual route by the Chichiklik pass; that by the Gez defile, and a variation of this by the interesting Bel Art pass which joins the Gez route from the north. Mr C. P. Skrine has an attractive description of the Bel Art in his book *Chinese Central Asia*, and had it not been that there was some doubt as to whether there was not still too much water in the Gez river I should have gone that way. As it was I chose a rather devious route of my own invention. Travelling by the Kara-tash pass to the north-east side of Muztagh Ata I would cross two little-known passes to the east of that mountain, the Tur-bulung and the Yangi Dawan, and then join the usual route at the Chichiklik 'maidan'. Apart from the opportunity of seeing the eastern side of Muztagh Ata I was drawn to this route by the absence of any red dotted line marking a known route over the Tur-bulung and by the fact that the name of the pass itself had an interrogation mark after it.

So far so good. From Tashkurghan to Gilgit, however, alternative routes are hard to find, for the only two obvious ways are those by the Mintaka or the Kilik passes, which hardly differ and which are both well known. But the conscientious traveller need not despair. If he casts his net wide enough some less obvious ways can be dragged in. There was one to be found by making a wide sweep to the east by the Oprang river and back into Hunza by the Shingshal gorge; but if wide sweeps had to be made there was a more attractive one for me to the west over the Wakhjir pass and then back into the extreme north-west corner of Hunza territory by either the Irshad or the Khora Bhort pass and down to Gilgit by the Karumbar nallah. The particular attraction of this route was that I should see not only the source of the Oxus and the Hindu Kush, but also the mountains north and west of our 'unexplored' glacier and so possibly get some idea of what lay in the wide gap between the head of the glacier and the Chillinji pass, a problem which we had expected to clear up in July.

It did, of course, occur to me that going by this route I should have to cross not only the Wakhjir pass and the great Central Asian water-parting, but also the frontier of Afghanistan of which Wakhan is part, and that in the present sorry scheme of things frontiers are apt to be more difficult to cross than passes. But I argued that Wakhan is a pretty remote part of Afghanistan where it was unlikely that I should meet any Afghan officials, that any Wakhis I had so far come across had seemed kind accommodating folk, and that by nipping smartly back into India from the vicinity of Bozai Gumbaz by the Irshad or Khora Bhort I should almost certainly avoid being caught up in the spider's web of passports, visas, and inquisitive officials. For it was unfortunately true that I had no Afghan visa nor any chance of obtaining one, but by going without I should merely be anticipating Mr Bevin's express wish for visa-less travel. In any case, if the worst happened, as usual much could be hoped for from time and chance.

At Tashkurghan I intended picking up our old friend Naiad Shah, for Wakhi was one of his five languages, which had, I hoped, been learnt more recently and perhaps less imperfectly than his Hindustani. I had found him faithful, helpful, stupid, and anxious to look after my interests without neglecting his own. He liked to travel with a few copper teapots and some rolls of cloth stowed away in his capacious saddle-bags with which he drove pretty hard bargains with the simple Kirghiz. But I also had a volunteer to go with me from Kashgar—a Turki from the considerable colony of gardeners and servants of all kinds which has thrived and multiplied exceedingly in the course of a few generations within the walls of the Consulate compound. It had occurred to him that it was his filial duty to look up his old father who was vaguely reported to keep a shop somewhere between Gilgit and Srinagar, and hearing that I was going that way he had thought that since he had no passport it would simplify matters if he travelled with me. I was not in a position myself to be particular about a trifle like that. Indeed, I was rather astonished that in remote Central Asia such sinister tokens of civilization should be expected from those whom we sweepingly classify as 'natives'. The world was evidently a grimmer place and had progressed more rapidly than I had thought. It was explained to Yusuf that I might not be going by the most direct route to Gilgit and Srinagar, but his ideas of geography were scattered and whether I went by Timbuktoo or Baghdad was all one to him so long as he could travel in the 'reserved' occupation of sahib's servant and so long as we eventually fetched up in Kashmir.

Yusuf had his own white pony of which he was very proud and very fond, but he had unfortunately no language but his own which was of no use at all to me. He carried bedding, and grain for the pony, and like Naiad Shah he had capacious saddle-bags which were crammed with goods for bartering on the road. The Eastern traveller seems to hold that a journey should not only be free of cost but also that it should show a profit—as witness the high proportion of travellers on Indian railways who neglect the formality of purchasing a ticket, and the profit a few of them make by robbing the paying passengers. I had my own baggage which amounted to a light pony-load for which I intended to hire transport from stage to stage. This obvious arrangement was, as it happened, a very foolish one, as it gave too many hostages to fortune; but I had not the spare cash to lay out on a pony for which in Kashgar I should have had to pay through the nose.

For the seventy miles from Kashgar to Ighiz Yar I got what was almost but not quite literally a flying start in the Consulate truck, costing the lives of a donkey, two dogs, and several hens. Yusuf who had gone ahead with the ponies met me there. We breakfasted in the dark before setting out early on 14 September with the outward-bound mail ponies with which we travelled until we turned off to the west up the Ghijak Sus. It was one of the thickest days I had seen, the sun peering wanly through a white fog of loess dust. We had a long climb the next day over the 13,000 ft. Ghijak pass before dropping to the narrow Kara-tash valley. As travelling companions we had a mob of yaks and donkeys one of which provided us, and even its Kirghiz owner, with a good laugh. Donkeys, as soon as they are off-loaded, love to have a roll; they usually stick half-way with their legs in the air without completing the roll. At the midday halt one of them started performing

on a steep slope and was amazed to find that he not only completed
the roll with ease, but continued rolling with increasing speed until
brought up with a terrible thump by a dry water course.

We halted for the night at Chat where there was a mixture of yorts,
mud-walled houses, and so many 'gumbaz' that the place looked like
a stack-yard. The people seemed to be Kirghiz and Turki hybrids,
unable to make up their minds whether to live in a yort or a house,
with the usual deplorable results consequent upon indecision. When
we crossed the valley and continued to the west up the long, winding
Kara-tash nallah we soon found ourselves in real Kirghiz country. It
was a very long march so that it was not until dusk that we reached the
last yorts below the Kara-tash pass at a height of about 15,000 ft. They
were tucked away on a shelf of grass out of sight from the track and
had it not been for the acrid smell of their yak-dung fires we should
have missed them. Here we found good entertainment notwithstand-
ing the presence of a large party of Turki grain merchants and their
donkeys. It was bitterly cold although early September and I found it
difficult to believe these folk who assured us that they lived there all
the winter.

The Kara-tash pass is 16,388 ft. high, only slightly lower than the
Ulugh Art, but neither of our ponies found the crossing difficult. There
was some snow, but except for the boulder-strewn summit it is an easy
pass for animals. Behind us a thick bank of loess haze reached up
almost to the level of the pass where a fierce gale was driving it back,
while to the west lowering rain clouds hung about the eastern face of
Muztagh Ata which I had wished so much to see. We descended easily
to the Ik-bel valley below, where on the far side of the river there were
a couple of yorts. Filling the valley head, a broad stream of unsul-
lied ice flowed gently downwards from a low ridge to the south. I was
tempted to embark on it, for it led in our direction, but hampered
as we were with ponies it would have been a chancey business. We
joined the grain merchants while they brewed tea, crouching round a
fire in the bitter wind, and then pushed on to the junction of the valley
with that of the Tur-bulung. Here I had expected to find yorts where I
could get some information about the Tur-bulung pass, but there was
no one there and so we went on until nightfall compelled us to camp
at the first grass.

Three hours further down we came to an 'aoul' (Kang Showar) and took up our quarters in a yort where there happened to be a scolding wife, a brawling husband, and a crying baby. The disadvantages of life in a yort were unmistakable. The Tur-bulung, we were told, was only fit for yaks, our ponies would have to go round by Subashi; but Yusuf, who so far had always ridden on top of his own baggage, volunteered to come with me provided he could have a yak to ride. Like any other Turki he was not much good on his feet and he had suffered from headache when crossing the Kara-tash.

We started back up the valley next day, Yusuf on one yak and our reduced amount of kit and a Kirghiz on another. The weather seemed set on balking me of one object of my journey, for it was a wretched day of low cloud and falling snow. However, the Tur-bulung valley itself was interesting enough for it contained a big glacier of the normal Himalayan type—debris-strewn, dirty, wrinkled—so different from the white, unblemished slabs of ice which are plastered on the west side of Muztagh Ata and on the slopes of Kungur. When level with the snout of this glacier our track turned away from the main valley to follow the Tur-bulung stream which here cuts its way down through a gorge from a hanging valley a thousand feet above. This upland valley was a wide, peaty bottom of coarse brown grass, like a typical Pamir valley. We were pressed to stop at one of the cleanest yorts I have ever seen, by a cheerful, bustling woman who lived there alone with a child; but it was too far from the pass, so having gratefully drunk tea and eaten maize bread and cream we pushed on to an 'aoul' of some dozen yorts at the head of the valley. We reached it at dusk—a dreary spot surrounded by bleak snow-covered hills and guarded by a pack of savage yellow dogs. I was bidden to mount a yak before approaching, and no one dared dismount before their owners had driven them off.

It snowed heavily throughout the night, but a cheerful banjo-playing youth assured us he would see us over the pass and down to the Chichiklik 'maidan' in spite of all. After a snowfall the response to reveille in a yort is amazingly prompt, for as soon as the cord of the felt covering the smoke-hole is pulled preparatory to lighting the fire, a small avalanche is released to overwhelm the occupants. When we started we could see nothing, not even the track, but the guide led on unerringly through low rounded hills until we realised we were on the pass, unmarked even by a pile of stones. It is, I imagine, something over 16,000 ft. and could be crossed by lightly laden ponies when clear of snow. We halted a thousand feet down the other side to give our yak some weeds and gravel before beginning the climb to the second pass, the Yangi Dawan, 16,100 ft. We reached this about 2 p.m. and looking down we could see the great plain of Chichiklik across the far end of which lay the main route to Tashkurghan. It was comparatively clear of snow, but though we looked long and hard neither yort nor yak could we see. The plain was empty of life.

All travellers from Sarikol to Kashgar or Yarkand who pass south of the Muztagh Ata range must traverse the Chichiklik 'maidan'. It lies at over 14,500 ft. and is in such an exposed position that only for a very short time in the year is it free from bitter winds and heavy snowfalls. Sir Aurel Stein discovered in the middle of the plain the ancient ruins of a hospice or serai. This had been mentioned by the Chinese Buddhist pilgrim Hsuan-tsang who described the Chichiklik as a 'region where icy storms rage. The ground, impregnated with salt, produces no crops, there are no trees and nothing but wretched herbs. Even at the time of the great heat the wind and snow continue. Merchant caravans in coming and going suffer severely in these difficult and dangerous spots.' According to Hsuan-tsang a great company of merchants and followers had once perished here, whereupon a saintly person of Tashkurghan, with the aid of the riches lost by this doomed caravan, built and endowed the hospice for the benefit of future travellers.

We descended to the plain and crossed it, with the ruins of this hospice away to our left, wondering at its emptiness and by no means relishing the prospect of a night out in such an inhospitable waste. A man with some donkeys was moving along the road and from him we learnt of the existence of a yort. Late in the evening we found it tucked away in a snow-filled hollow of the hills on the western edge of the plain. A very miserable place it was too; but any clothes will fit a naked man, and on the Chichiklik 'maidan' in September any roof is better than none. The family of the yort seemed to be trying to live like Kirghiz without the essential stock which alone enables the Kirghiz to exist. Their sole livestock were six sheep, and they seemed to eke out a precarious existence by sheltering (though not feeding) rare travellers like ourselves who had failed to make the usual stage. Though I

On Muztagh Ata (*c.* 17,000 ft.)—the blessings of marriage,
or Consul and Consolation

Muztagh Ata—our ridge and snowy pleasure-dome right of centre

Chinese soldiers and Kirghiz hunter at Mintaka Karaul

Kirghiz

Kirghiz woman wearing a party hat

Inside a yort—Naiad Shah second from left with Chinese soldier on his left

am all for preserving un-disfigured the beauties of the natural scene, I thought that here was a good case for a modest advertisement. Had we not by chance met the donkey-man we should have spent a perishing cold night and they would have been so much the worse off.

Poverty by no means always implies dirt though it often goes with a large family. Here there was a large and a very dirty family, and though a well populated head is held to be the sign of a generous mind I took what few precautions I could to avoid that distinction. From the 'maidan' the road climbed for some miles before beginning its plunge through the Dershat gorge to the Tashkurghan valley. It was another day of cold wind and sleet which chilled us to the bone before we could enter the sheltering wall of the gorge—a loathsome, waterless, bone-yard of a place, littered with the dried bodies and bare skeletons of donkeys, ponies, and camels. The ascent to the Chichiklik from this side is nearly 5000 ft. There is no water, and the track is such as to break the heart of the stoutest beast. Most of the donkeys of Sinkiang must die in harness, laying their bones by the side of some such cruel road as this.

Just before we reached the 12,000 ft. level we ran into fine weather. White fleecy clouds cast their racing black shadows over the yellowing fields of the Tagharma vale, while the river which a month ago ran brown and turgid now flashed clear and blue. Nearing the first village nine miles out from Tashkurghan, we were surprised to see the ponies coming out to meet us—a neat piece of staff work for which the ponymen must be given the credit. Not knowing much about the route I had told them we should be four days in crossing, but when they reached this village and heard that the Tur-bulung was only three days' journey they had off-loaded and brought the ponies back to meet us. We joined them at the serai where the loads had been dumped and enjoyed the finest mutton I have ever tasted.

We had a day's rest at Tashkurghan while Naiad Shah fettled up himself and his pony for the Wakhan trip. As I was no longer under the aegis of the Consul in person I was at once humiliated and relieved by the absence of any offers of hospitality. The magistrate and a few Chinese officers waited on me, but the meeting was short and cool, their former deference being nicely readjusted to meet my new circumstances and my slightly more travel-stained appearance. There was some uncalled for inquisitiveness about Yusuf's passport, or his lack of one, and passes for the returning pony-men had to be obtained. I felt that I might as well be in Europe.

At the Taghlak Gumbaz, the first stage out, the yort had been removed so that this time we were obliged to cook inside the monument. Any feelings we may have had that we were desecrating the tomb were easily suppressed. At Dafdar we enjoyed excellent fare in the house to which our former friends of the yort had now removed against the approach of winter. Reaping was almost over, threshing and winnowing were in full swing, and there was the genial air of prosperity and abundance usually attendant upon harvest time. The inside of a mud-walled house is, however, not nearly so pleasant as that of a yort. There is no light at all except when the door is open, while instead of lying luxuriously on the floor round the fire one must sit primly on the hard clay platform which serves as both bed and seat.

At Beyik I was surprised and displeased to find that the former Chinese post had been withdrawn and that a detachment of soldiers had been moved up to Mintaka Karaul. I had some fear that when the Chinese saw us heading for the Wakhjir instead of the Mintaka pass they might try to stop us. There were only two yorts here, one occupied by Tajiks the other by Kirghiz. We stopped at the latter, and an excellent, lively, good-humoured woman who ruled the roost made us one of the flaky pastry, cream-smeared loaves for supper. Even in a yort punctilious ceremony is observed, and it was amusing to see our heterogeneous assembly—Kirghiz, Hunza, Turkoman, Englishman—gather preparatory to eating while our host went the rounds with a long-spouted ewer as each in turn held out his hands to wash. One dried them by the simple expedient of crossing the arms, squeezing the hands under the opposite armpits, and then withdrawing them swiftly to wipe off the moisture. When we had finished, at a signal from the reverend Naiad Shah, we raised our hands in a supplicatory attitude and then brought them down together as though stroking the beard, muttering at the same time the appropriate grace.

Between Beyik and Mintaka Karaul, Naiad Shah took us a short way up a side nallah to visit the yort of a Hunza woman who had married a Kirghiz with whom he hoped to do some trade. We timed our arrival well. She had just finished baking so we gorged ourselves on hot fresh bread and firm, fresh yoghourt. The road from Tashkurghan to Mintaka is I think, the finest stretch of 'yoghourt' road in the country. Here it is solid enough to be eaten only with a spoon, whereas up north it is altogether a thinner brew usually of what cooks call a 'pouring consistency'.

As if to remind me that life had its rubs and was not all yoghourt and skittles, I came an imperial cropper that afternoon as I was trying to cross a stream by leaping from boulder to boulder. One of my rubber-soled 'expedition' boots slipped and ice-axe, wrist-watch, and a tin of tobacco went to the bottom. They were all recovered, but Naiad Shah, knowing my fondness for water, thought I had done it on purpose; nor did I trouble to undeceive him.

We marched past the Chinese post, telling them merely that we should look in later, and went on to the yorts a mile or so up the Mintaka valley. These people knew Naiad Shah well and readily agreed to provide a yak for my baggage and a guide to take us over the Wakhjir. The carcass of a sheep which had recently been slaughtered was produced and the whole party fell to work stripping it bare. I have seldom met anyone, not excepting meat-starved Kavirondos, so avid for meat as the Kirghiz. Men, women, and toothless infants gnaw away at bones like so many dogs.

As we wished to proceed up the Wakhjir valley there was no escaping the Chinese post, so positioned as to command views up both valleys. One could make a short cut a mile or two away from the post, but it was no more possible to leave the Mintaka route and head for the Wakhjir without attracting attention than it would be to do a striptease act unobserved in Hyde Park. To call on the officer at the post seemed to be the boldest course and the best. In order to counter any objections on his part I armed Naiad Shah with a bottle of Russian brandy I had with me, which he was told on no account to produce unless the Chinese began raising difficulties. Frankness and goodfellowship must be the approach to this far-flung Celestial.

Our start was delayed. The ponies had strayed up the hill, while Naiad Shah was dodging from yort to yort busy picking up unconsidered trifles, a bit of meat here, a skinful of yoghourt there—the latter was tied to his saddle where it gurgled musically. It was ten o'clock before we reached the post where we were told that the commanding officer was still in bed. It seemed a pity to waken him so we began to unfold our plans in a casual way to a subordinate of unknown rank. He seemed a bit surprised. No objections were even hinted at. The only condition was that a Chinese soldier would have to accompany us for the first day to ward off the attacks of Russian Kirghiz. I was therefore surprised and annoyed when Naiad Shah before I could stop him pro-duced the bottle with a flourish from under his coat and handed it to the astonished Chinaman with the air of a prince bestowing a princely gift—as indeed it was. Gratifying as it must be to the one party there is nothing so annoying to the other as having made an unnecessary bribe, particularly when the bribe in question might have been put to a hundred better uses. One at any rate I thought of, even as the China-man accepted the precious gift with disgusting indifference.

Before the commanding officer could be awakened to see what Santa Claus Naiad Shah had brought, and possibly to make inquiries about our plans, I got the party mounted and rode off. An hour later, looking back, I saw a small cloud of dust. Presently the thud of hoofs could be heard and we were overtaken by our armed escort of one. As it is irksome to the Chinese cavalryman to move on the wide open spaces of Sinkiang at anything less than a gallop, soon our modest pace exhausted his patience and off he went. I had half-feared that this annihilator of space might be the bearer of orders for our return, but to my relief he brought nothing, not even thanks for our costly mis-take. At last, I thought with complacence, we were clear of soldiers and frontier posts. There were none on the Wakhjir pass and certainly none on the Irshad. On the Wakhan Pamir we should, no doubt, meet friendly Kirghiz, and perhaps at Bozai Gumbaz a few rude tillers of the soil who would gladly speed us on our way and ask no questions. Life seemed very good.

CHAPTER XIV

THE OXUS SOURCE

———◆———

THE WAKHJIR IS A FINE OPEN VALLEY, comparatively rich in grass. Nevertheless, it was then uninhabited—at least neither Kirghiz nor Chinese knew of anyone living there. Its position is isolated and close to the Russian frontier and in the past it had attracted the attention of raiders who used to enter by way of the Tigurman Su pass. At the foot of the nallah which leads to this pass we stopped for lunch. I bathed in a clear deep pool and found that the midday sun even at the end of September was still hot enough to dry one. A little beyond on the other side of the valley is the Kilik nallah and the path leading to the pass of that name. A deserted Chinese fort stands at the entrance.

The horns of *Ovis poli*, the great mountain sheep, lie scattered thickly in the upper Wakhjir. These sheep range over a wide area in Central Asia, but the Pamirs are their favourite haunt. A head was first brought to Europe by Wood, the first Englishman to explore the Oxus, and the beast was so named in compliment to Marco Polo's original description. In Sarakul there are many cairns of *Ovis poli* heads which have been collected and stacked by the Kirghiz, just as in other days their ancestors under Gengiz Khan liked to build mounds and pyramids of the skulls of their enemies.

Naiad Shah had promised that that night we should sleep at a 'gumbaz', but the sun sank, the valley narrowed, and the little glacier of Khush Bel came into view without any sign of it. Instead we had to pitch our tents in a hollow while there was still light by which to gather fuel, and even as we did so we saw to our astonishment a couple of Kirghiz on yaks apparently bent on the same errand. Their yorts, they said, were five miles further on. They had arrived there two days before from the direction of Bozai Gumbaz and the Chakmaktin Lake, a region they were now quitting in fear of raiders from the Russian side. On a clear moonlit night we sat by the fire until driven to bed by the cold. In the night the weather changed. We woke to a dull snowy morning with snow on the ground, so, foregoing our breakfasts, we set off hot-foot for the yorts, passing Naiad Shah's 'gumbaz' on the way. Triumphantly he pointed this out to me, for he thought, quite rightly as it happened, that on the previous evening I had not believed him.

There were three yorts, or more correctly the walls of three. Their roofs had not yet been put on because the owners were in transit, bound for lower down the valley. Snow drifted through the open roof while men, women, and children huddled down under the walls to shelter from the wind. They were in much better plight than refugees usually are, having with them all their goods and chattels and a house to put them in. Outside stood their yaks and their horses, busy scraping away the snow in search of grass. Emigrants would be a better description of them, for they intended leaving Wakhan for good and settling in Chinese territory. Their yaks seemed to me bigger and more powerful than any I had seen—some might have rivalled the Durham ox itself.

After food and talk we learnt that a party of men and five yaks were returning to Bozai Gumbaz to fetch the remainder of their goods. We therefore shifted our loads to these, sent the Mintaka man home, and started for the Wakhjir. The pass is only just over 16,000 ft. but I found it perishing cold in spite of wearing a 'poshteen'—a sheep-skin coat—on top of my windproofs. Descending a valley on our right, from what we were told was the Kara Jilga pass, were streams of laden yaks, ponies, and sheep. Thirty families were said to be moving out of the enclave east of the Chakmaktin Lake with the intention of settling in Chinese territory. I wondered if they, too, had passports.

The ascent to the pass is gradual, finally flattening out to a broad saddle just below the summit containing a considerable lake about half a mile long and 200 or 300 yards across. From it the Wakhjir river flows to the east. Overlooking the pass on the south is a fine snow mountain of over 19,000 ft.—the eastern extremity of the Hindu Kush. As we descended into Wakhan the clouds melted, the sun came out and far below we saw the thin blue ribbon of the infant Oxus winding through a wide shingle bed, edged in places with grass the colour of old gold, and flanked on the north by the smooth, brown slopes of the Wakhan Pamir and on the south by the bold snow-covered Hindu Kush. Sheltered behind a 'gumbaz' built on a grass shelf near the foot of the pass I sat and gazed wonderingly at the snout of a large glacier two or three miles upstream whence from a black ice cave emerged the new-born Oxus. Here the river is called the Ab-i-Wakhan.

The question of the true source of the Oxus once aroused as much interest and controversy as did the problem of the Nile sources. Perhaps even more, because which of the upper confluents of the Oxus was the parent stream was of political importance, for it was that stream that was to mark the boundary between Russia and Afghanistan. Where there are several confluents with fairly equal pretensions the first discoverer of each naturally presses the claims of his to be the true and only source. Explorers are sensitive about their discoveries and should these affect the location of international boundaries then controversy may be long and bitter.

Wood's great journey of 1838 and his discovery of the lake to which he gave the name Victoria (see Wood's *Journey to the Source of the Oxus*) was thought to have settled the matter, and the Pamir river issuing from that lake was held to be the true parent stream. It was upon this geographical basis that the Boundary Agreement of 1872 with Russia was made. The next claimant was the not very significant stream which joins the Ab-i-Wakhan, twenty-five miles below its glacier source. This stream, the Little Pamir, rises in hills near the western end of the Chakmaktin lake. To add to the confusion this same lake is the true source of the Murghab or Ak-su which, emerging from the eastern end of the lake, describes a great loop north round the Pamirs in Russian territory and enters the Oxus in the big bend a hundred miles north of Ishkashim. For many years this was held to be the main river by reason of its greater length and volume compared with that of the Ab-i-Wakhan. The difference in length, if anything at all, is but a few miles, and the volume varies with the season. Both points were disputed very strongly by Lord Curzon who in 1894 crossed the Wakhjir, visited the ice-cave giving birth to the river, and followed it downwards as far as Sarhad. His exhaustive description and discussion of the rival claims from every possible angle appeared in the *Geographical Journals* for July, August, and September 1896. The question is now of purely academic interest. My opinion is worth little, but to my mind, speaking as a mountaineer, the only fit and proper birthplace for this mighty river of most ancient fame is the ice-cave in the glacier at the eastern extremity of the Hindu Kush, at the innermost heart of Central Asia.

For it is a river whose waters, to use Lord Curzon's words, 'tell of forgotten peoples and secrets of unknown lands, and are believed to have rocked the cradle of our race'.

We passed some more Kirghiz families on their way over the Wakhjir, and then having reached the valley we turned upstream to some yorts tucked away between moraine and river bank not more than a mile or so from the glacier source. Though the Kirghiz with whom we were travelling were friendly enough, we fell into such poor hands here that I wondered which of them was truly representative of the Kirghiz of Wakhan. There were only two yorts—a large and a small. We naturally went to the first, but our reception was so cool that we were obliged to resort to the smaller where the sole occupant turned out to be an orphan girl about fourteen years old. All we got was a little milk which we eked out with the hard lumps of 'karut' which the Kirghiz had brought with them. One sees balls of this stuff being dried on racks outside most yorts. It is made from the surplus yoghourt and it looks and tastes like solidified sawdust with a faintly bitter suspicion of cheese. Much of it is sold in Kashgar where it is used for flavouring soups, while the Kirghiz take it on a journey as a haversack ration.

We made a short march of only eight miles next day to some yorts on the south bank of the river where the Kama Su nallah joins it. There is a pass leading from here over the Hindu Kush to Misgar and I was tempted to try it in case my assumption about the absence of officials in Wakhan proved to be ill-founded. My information was that it was already blocked by winter snow, but in point of fact I could not face a repetition of the journey between Misgar and Gilgit, particularly as by going that way I should miss seeing the country near the Chillinji pass in which I was more interested. There is a lot of peat in the Ab-i-Wakhan valley hereabouts and that night we had a glorious peat fire in the yort. Naiad Shah got on very well with these people; his saddle-bags were opened and trade begun with the headman—an intelligent man who proved to be a bit of a mechanic. He had a complete set of tools and mended a broken pin on my watch in a workmanlike way. From him we began to hear the first mutterings about our uncertain future—the difficulty of the Irshad pass and the Afghan spies at Bozai Gumbaz. Such talk, I think, infected Naiad Shah who probably now began to evolve a private plan for himself in case mine miscarried.

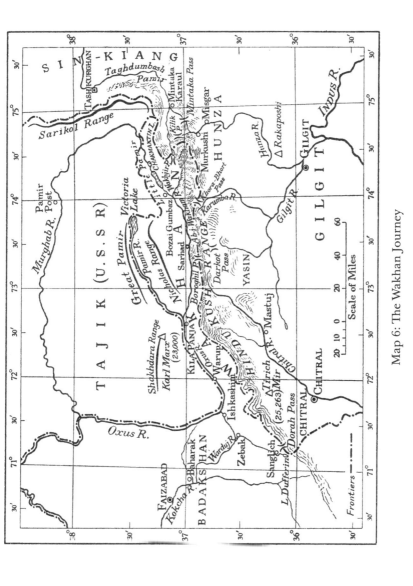

Map 6: The Wakhan Journey

Neither he nor Yusuf, I'm afraid, was a lover of variety; neither cared at all how often he followed the beaten track.

For the seventeen miles to Bozai Gumbaz the track follows the right bank of the river where for the first few miles there is abundance of grass, brown and withering now before the onset of autumn. On the south bank the snow on the slopes of the Hindu Kush came down to below 14,000 ft. Apart from one small homestead where an attempt was being made to grow barley there were no habitations; the two villages marked on the map did not appear to exist and their names were not known. Some stacks of peat drying on the south bank suggested that possibly there were more people about in summer. At the present time, however, there were more 'gumbaz' than people, for I counted at least a dozen of these queer conical mud cupolas, built on a low square foundation, between the foot of the Wakhjir pass and Bozai Gumbaz. Here, on the wide grass and gravel plain between the Little Pamir river and the Ab-i-Wakhan, at the junction of two important routes, there is nothing whatever but a cluster of these 'gumbaz'. They are apparently of no antiquity and according to Lord Curzon are the tomb and memorial of one Bozai, a local chief who was killed in a fight with Hunza raiders about 1850.

From the vicinity of the pass we had been accompanied by a young Kirghiz mounted on a good-looking horse which he shared with one whom I took to be some sort of dependent, for the young man had about him an air of authority. We discovered that he was the son of the local chieftain whose 'aoul' was on the slopes across the Little Pamir river about three miles from Bozai Gumbaz. For a chief's son he was not an imposing figure; he was short-sighted and wore dark glasses which, I thought, would do little to alleviate this particular affliction. His chief claim to admiration was his very fine round velvet hat trimmed with fox fur. At first he had seemed rather stand-offish, but now he became quite affable and assured us that he would see to it that we got yaks for our journey over either the Irshad or Khora Bhort pass.

Two or three miles above its junction with the Ab-i-Wakhan we forded the Little Pamir river which was muddy and meandering—not to be compared either in beauty or volume to the blue, rushing Ab-i-Wakhan. The valley itself is wide and flat and stretches a great way until finally it is shut in by mountains far to the east, so that I could understand how travellers coming up the river might well mistake this branch for the main valley. Indeed, this is the obvious and most direct way to Tashkurghan. It is a route which is open at all seasons, and in former days when travellers had not to consider international boundaries in their choice of route it was no doubt more frequented than the Wakhjir route.

Having climbed for two or three miles up rough grass slopes we came to the chief's 'aoul' and were ushered into an empty yort reserved apparently for guests. By the grazing herds dotted all over the landscape I concluded the chief was a man of substance, spacious in the possession of yaks. The son brought tea and a bowl of cream and Naiad Shah once again opened the question of hiring yaks in the hope of clinching the matter there and then. To our disgust he said that he must first ask his father. Father was out, counting his flocks and herds I presumed. When he did arrive he was not at all the sort of patriarch I had hoped to see. He was short and stout with a bluff John Bull air which agreed ill with his cunning blood-shot pig eyes.

He was obdurate from the start. He would not hear of our going by such an irregular route. We must go to Sarhad forty miles away to report to the Afghan official who would then send us out by the usual route over the Boroghil pass. We pointed out that while we should be charmed to meet the Afghan, to go to Sarhad would cause us serious inconvenience and loss of time, and that since no one yet knew we were here no one need ever know which way we had gone. Neither argument nor entreaty had the least effect. On the Irshad pass side of his head he was stone deaf. Should the Afghan official hear of our going out by the back door, as he assuredly would, he, the local authority, would be held responsible and would suffer penalties. I tried another tack and chaffed him about the thirty Kirghiz families, his neighbours for whom he was probably responsible, who were now entering Chinese territory without permission; but he heartily approved of that incursion on the grounds that humanity knows no frontiers. When asked why they were moving he replied cryptically that Kirghiz, Chinese, and English were all brothers. The relationship was not flattering, but I took his point.

I went to bed in very ill humour, still hoping that in the morning he would prove more accommodating, or that Naiad Shah would show more spirit or suggest some way of conciliating this Tartar. So far he had merely acquiesced in everything said, having already made up his mind that he, for one, was going back by the Wakhjir. I discovered later that he had bartered some cloth at the last yort for twelve seers of butter which he had arranged to pick up on the way back. Every man is supposed to have his price, but it did not occur to me to try to bribe Father, for paper money would have had no attractions for one whose real wealth was probably immense, and although a camera or a watch might have tempted him I did not think the occasion called for such a sacrifice. After all it was only forty miles to Sarhad, and when the Afghan there had got over his surprise and, possibly, delight at meeting strangers, he would probably be glad enough to get rid of us by the shortest route. Even from the Boroghil route we could still traverse back on the other side of the Hindu Kush to the Chillinji pass with the loss of no more than a few days. However, the time for bribery had gone, for according to Naiad Shah this 'unconversable horse-belching Tartar' had already queered his pitch and mine by sending a swift messenger to Sarhad with news of the English invasion.

In the morning Father was no more agreeable. We sat talking about this and that amicably enough, while he admired my camera and looked into the film window expecting to see a picture, but when we returned to the question of routes 'Sarhad' was all he could say. Finally I gave in, and rather grudgingly and with some delay he found us one yak out of his many hundreds. To Naiad Shah I gave his wages and a very perfunctory blessing, for I thought, possibly wrongly, that he had shown neither zeal nor skill in playing an admittedly weak hand. All the indignation and vindictiveness that I felt for Father as the blighter of my cherished hopes, fell, as it usually does in these cases, on the luckless interpreter. All this argument about routes had passed over Yusuf's head. He took no part and seemed not to mind Naiad Shah's desertion, for his confidence in the sanctity of his 'reserved' occupation of sahib's servant seemed still unshaken.

We rode down to the junction and joined the track which follows the right bank of the river to Sarhad. Almost immediately below the junction the combined streams enter a gorge which continues with but one intermission to Sarhad nearly forty miles away. On the one bank bands of green and vermilion rock and on the other slopes of snow made the scene weird and wild. Two or three miles down on a

Mosque and market square, Kashgar

'V.J. Day' at Kashgar

Yort

Kirghiz women sewing wool
tassels on roof of yort

Inside a yort

Typical debris-free glacier of
the Muztagh Ata range near the
Ulugh Art pass

rock knoll above the river is a 'gumbaz' of roughly hewn stone. This is Karwan Balasi which Sir Aurel Stein identified as the 'Hall of the Red Buddha' mentioned in the account of the successful expedition of the Chinese general, Kao Hsien Chi, against a Tibetan army in Yasin in the year A.D. 747. This remarkable man marched three columns from Sinkiang by different routes, concentrated them at Sarhad, crossed the Boroghil and the Darkot (15,400 ft.) passes in the face of strong opposition, and led his victorious force down through Yasin to Gilgit.

At this point I noticed on the south side of the river the track which leads to the Kirghiz 'aoul' of Baikra and thence in one day to the Irshad or Khora Bhort pass. I halted our small party and sat down to think things out. Naiad Shah's example infected me; like him I began to wonder whether we had not seen enough of Wakhan and this appeared to be our last chance of getting out. But how? The yak driver had his orders which he dared not disobey, and if I abandoned the yak and my kit, within an hour the driver would be telling his story to Father who would be quite capable of having us stopped. From this it followed inexorably that the driver must be rendered incapable of movement or somehow eliminated, and I had got as far as pondering the questionable wisdom of this step and whether Yusuf would be either a willing or a useful accomplice in crimes of violence, when a party of men and yaks appeared coming up the gorge. As the omens were evidently unpropitious, with a troubled mind I gave the order to go on.

Some ten miles down, the barrenness of the gorge is interrupted by an extensive grass 'maidan'. Here yaks were grazing and at the far end was a small Tajik settlement. We rode up to it, for now I had a vague hope that by taking advantage of a full moon we might persuade them to help us to do a moonlight flit to Baikra and thence across the border. But there were too many people about for any private conversation; there were several mounted Kirghiz visitors and a number of newly arrived Tajik settlers busy building a stone house.

From this point the gorge closed in relentlessly. 'Beyond Hyde Park', said Sir Fopling Flutter, 'all is desert', and beyond here all is gorge on a violent and stupendous scale. By dark, when we had made good fifteen of the forty miles to Sarhad which I was bent on reaching next day in order to put our fortunes quickly to the test, we reached Langar where there is a 'gumbaz'. We went inside to cook. At 2 a.m. of a bright moonlight night we started again. Gorges and deserts are best traversed by night, and when day broke, except for a graceful snow spire on the south side, nothing was revealed that would not better have remained hidden in the soft obscurity of moonlight.

The track lay a thousand feet above the river, but some twelve miles from Langar we were obliged to descend to river-level to cross the Dara Jilga coming down from the Nicholas range to the north. The ford, a dangerous one full of boulders, was taken by the yak without a stumble, but Yusuf 's nag which I was riding came down twice, nearly drowning himself and his rider. Yusuf wisely went round by a foot-bridge. Having laboriously regained the height we had lost, we had breakfast. It was 9 a.m., more than half the journey had been done, but now the mountains were drawing in closer and steeper about the river, forcing the path farther away and ever higher, until at last it left the river altogether to cross a great projecting spur by the high Daliz pass.

The pass was steep and deep in snow, both yak and pony were by now tired and lagging, and near the top when I was well ahead and alone, I met two men on foot—a dirty, unsavoury pair, one of whom seemed to be wearing some semblance of a uniform. Their manners were no better than their appearance. They shouted at me truculently and unintelligibly, so I waved them airily in the direction of my followers and passed on. This would not do. They came after me shouting still louder at which I turned round. One of them bawled out questioningly 'Russi?' To which I, not caring much what they might think, made a gesture indicative of assent. The effect was all that I could have wished. Without a word they turned and went on their way.

On the other side where the track begins to drop steeply down a stony gully, I sat down to wait for the others whom to my disgust I saw were now accompanied by the two low comedians. The passportless Yusuf, hearing already the clank of chains, informed me in his most mournful tones that they were two policemen who had been sent to look for us. The word 'police' seems to be current in these parts and it had an unwelcome sound. Not that I felt a criminal, but in the last month or so I had seen something of Central Asiatic police and soldiers and had not liked what I had seen. A slovenly uniform and a rifle of antique European make are their stock in trade. Having done so much, Authority then considers it has done enough—that it has in fact provided for them handsomely—which is perfectly correct. For, armed with the power which such things confer, their possessors need take little thought for the morrow what they shall eat or what they shall drink, for any Kirghiz, Turki, or Wakhi, who is not in uniform must provide. The police at Sarhad proved to be true to this dirty, parasitic type—a queer mixture of buffoonery and brutality.

At Sarhad the Oxus bursts from the gorge and, rejoicing in its freedom, spreads in meandering streams over a wide flat stony valley. The valley-floor is in fact all river-bed so that the cultivated land lies on the lower slopes of the hills where small streams fed from the snows above can be used to irrigate the fields. Wheat, a beardless barley, beans and peas, are grown, and since the height is over 10,000 ft. it follows that the valley must be a regular sun-trap. Even so in early October many of the crops were not yet harvested. On the north side, where all the cultivation lies, there are some half-dozen widely scattered villages of mud and stone houses each with its inevitable patch of white poplar saplings. Opposite on the south side a wide green valley leads gently to a broad gap flanked by a noble array of snow mountains—the Boroghil pass, the high road to India.

Lying thus on the route from India and on that from Badak-shan by the Oxus valley, Sarhad is of some importance, for it is the last place at which east-bound travellers can obtain grain before crossing the Pamirs and reaching the oases of Sinkiang. In accordance with this importance the Afghans have here a frontier post of police and soldiers under a 'sirdar' whose duty and pleasure it is to obstruct all travellers, however important or however insignificant, and whether they are provided with credentials or not. In 1890 Mr and Mrs Littledale (the first and probably the only English lady to visit the Pamirs) were detained for twelve days, and four years later Lord Curzon, who was a guest of the Amir who had himself warned the post of his guest's coming, would have been detained, too, as a Russian spy had not his party been in superior numbers to the Afghans. He reported the too zealous 'sirdar' to the Amir and the sequel he relates as follows: 'The Amir instituted inquiries and the reply of the now frightened "sirdar" was really so ingenious as to extort my reluctant admiration. "He was still awaiting", he said, "the arrival of the great English lord sahib, whose coming had been announced by His Majesty the Amir, and who would no doubt appear in uniform with an escort of a thousand men. In the meantime two of the lord sahib's servants (i.e. Curzon and his companion Lennard) had already passed through with an insignificant following. He himself would continue diligently to await the great lord". I heard afterwards that this polite intention on the part of the sirdar had been frustrated by an imperative summons to Kabul; but what may have since transpired I do not know.'

CHAPTER XV

SARHAD TO ISHKASHIM
—OPEN ARREST

◆

THOUGH THE TEMPO OF CHANGE nowadays is everywhere rapid, in the East change is traditionally slower. As it had been the custom to detain travellers at Sarhad fifty years ago then assuredly they would be detained to-day. But I was not to know that. Had I been aware how strait was the way, how fine the mesh, I should certainly have withdrawn discreetly with Naiad Shah by way of the Wakhjir; but as it was I marched more or less blithely, though very tired, to my fate. The first house we came to was the police barracks which promptly emitted a noisy crowd of seedy, undersized ruffians (at Sarhad there are more police than inhabitants) eager to congratulate our captors and to inspect the captives, for so I suspected we had now become. The Afghan commander's house, to which we had to go, was a mile or so further on. The inhabitants were too busy with their threshing and winnowing to care about us, but the police alone were numerous enough to play the part of the crowd at what might have been the triumph of one of the less successful of the Roman Consuls, whose poor best was one disconsolate shaggy barbarian and his smooth but still more disconsolate slave.

Presently the 'sirdar', whom I took to be a Pathan, appeared clad in a smartly cut grey greatcoat with brass buttons. He spoke only Pushtu so neither he, nor Yusuf, nor I, had any pleasantries to exchange. He gave us one cold look, the word 'Ingreze' was spoken by someone, either in extenuation or reproach, and he strode away to his house. He was a tall dignified looking chap with hook nose and severe eyes—a stern path-of-duty man, I felt—who in his subsequent rare appearances outside stalked gravely round, a blue turban on his head and a flowing 'chapkan' flung loosely over his shoulders. He looked somewhat like a young but earnest bird-of-prey whose dignity was only slightly impaired by the squalor of his cage, which was a mud and stone hovel, distinguishable from the others by the presence of window frames, one covered with nothing and the other with paper. This house also did duty as an office, to which there came a surprising number of callers at all hours of the day. Behind was another hovel which served as kitchen and guard-room combined where the police on duty waited patiently for the bird-of-prey's calls for tea or for a crime to be committed. I pitched my tent outside and a guard was immediately posted.

Next morning as I was breakfasting at the tent door in the sun the 'sirdar' emerged, made a leisurely survey of his domain, and then stalked gravely over to his prisoners. One of his myrmidons had a few words of vile Hindustani and through this unsatisfactory medium I was given to understand that we must remain here until orders for our release or disposal had come from the Commissar (ominous word) at Ishkashim. Hastily scanning my map, which came to an end eighty miles west of Sarhad, I could find no trace of Ishkashim until in the margin in small lettering I read: 'Ishkashim 30 m.' My heart sank. The distance alone, coupled with the presence of a 'Commissar', boded no good. As Mrs Elton remarked of Birmingham: 'One had not great hopes of Ishkashim. I always say there is something direful in the sound.' And how long would I have to wait for this permission? Four days, they said, and a messenger had already left. It seemed little enough for a journey of over a hundred miles each way and I wondered whether a messenger had really gone or whether this was merely a conventional opening calling for a bid. But the aspect of the bird-of-prey was not encouraging in that respect.

We were quite ready for a day off, so the first day of our captivity passed away pleasantly enough as I lay in the sun reading and smoking. Ignorant of how seriously our captors regarded their prize I began to look about for a mountain to climb; if four days must be spent here they might be well spent, but on this side was nothing but slag heaps and scree slopes, all the climb-worthy mountains were on the other side of the river and to reach them I would need transport and a camp. I thought I might become a ticket-of-leave man by asking the 'sirdar' for a few days leave to explore the surrounding country, which, since (as I learnt later) I was regarded as a dangerous spy, was an assumption not unlike that of the boy who having murdered his parents asked to be acquitted on the grounds that he was an orphan.

Next morning the bird-of-prey again stepped over to my tent for his morning cigarette, this time alone. I was ready for him, and began playing ostentatiously with a spare watch I had with me. When this evoked no sign of interest I was reduced to making vulgar movements of thumb and fingers suggestive of the passing of money. He was not agreeably impressed by this, for he sent for his Hindustani scholar and asked sharply what I meant. I quickly changed the subject, for he was either that *rara avis* an incorruptible official, or else he really had sent word to his superior at Ishkashim and was no longer a free agent. All these people, I thought (Father had done the same) act too impetuously and are too eager to divest themselves of responsibility, thus depriving themselves of the possibility of hearing something to their advantage.

After this rebuff I went for a walk to cool off, but I had not gone a hundred yards before a couple of police were in pursuit clutching at me. Who did I think I was to go wandering about Wakhan like this? High words passed, and to prevent being dragged back I staged a sit down strike which had the effect of making one of them go back for instructions. I was allowed to make a restricted tour of the village accompanied by a guard.

About midday on the third day I was greatly surprised by hearing that a messenger from Ishkashim had just arrived. It seemed hardly possible, but so it was. However, nothing (except the journey) was to be done in a hurry and an hour passed before the bird-of-prey flapped his way slowly and solemnly to my tent. I had some misgivings as to the purport of the message, but hope was uppermost. I rose and greeted the 'sirdar', trying hard to suppress a smile of satisfaction at our impending release and succeeding quite easily when I learnt that the Boroghil was not for us, but that we were to go to Ishkashim and thence, if we were lucky, out by Chitral. This was bad news. Even if we were allowed to go out by Chitral we should be still farther from Gilgit where there was my kit and two months' mail, but I feared even more that the same gambit would be played again. I saw ourselves passing through the whole hierarchy of Afghan officials, each curious to see the English spy, each afraid to let us go, until finally we reached the fountain-head at Kabul, heaven alone knew how many weeks' journey away. I was concerned for poor Yusuf who had to get himself and his pony to Srinagar and back to Kashgar before the passes closed, and more nearly for myself since tobacco and sugar were running short. There was no help for it. A fat donkey was provided for my kit and after the coolest of farewells off we went in charge of the inevitable escort of two blackguards on one pony.

However uncertain our future I rejoiced to be once more on the move and on a route both historic and unusual. Although the upper Oxus valleys have been visited by many, few Europeans and possibly no Englishman have followed the valley as far as Ishkashim since Wood made his famous journey to Victoria Lake a hundred years ago. A great many travellers have seen the valley above Sarhad and a few have been down to Kila Panja where the Pamir river from Victoria Lake joins the main stream. In 1873 Col. Gordon's party of the Forsyth Mission to Kashgar went down to Kila Panja where they were stopped, but a native surveyor, travelling under the obscure generic title of the 'Munshi', went on to do a remarkable journey, following the river for a hundred miles beyond Ishkashim, before returning to India via Kabul. The 'Mirza' was another of these nameless explorers who were sent out by the Indian Survey Department in the latter half of the last century to unravel geographical problems in remote transfrontier regions inaccessible to Europeans. In 1868–69 the 'Mirza' made a route-survey from Faizabad to Ishkashim, thence up the Oxus to the Chakmaktin lake and across the Pamirs to Kashgar, finally returning to India by Yarkand and the Karakoram pass. The most noted of these 'pundits', as they were called, were two men from Milam in Garhwal, Nain Singh and Kishen Singh, or 'A-K', to give him his more famous name, both of whom explored extensively in Tibet in the 1860s and 1870s.

We forded the river to the south side without difficulty and stopped for the night at a little hamlet by some wonderfully clear springs some ten miles from Sarhad. It became bitterly cold as soon as the sun disappeared. Beyond bawling their loudest when they wanted us to stop or go on, our escort, of whom only one had a rifle, was not overbearing, though the armed man never let me out of his sight, sticking closer than a brother. At night, curiously enough, he assumed that no sane man would think of running away. I was allowed to sleep in the tent while they and Yusuf took up snugger and dirtier quarters in some house. Undesirable though their company was in such strange and interesting surroundings, it meant that I could cast aside dull care and leave them, the agents of the Afghan government whose guest I was, to worry about food, shelter, and transport for my kit if not for myself. And I must say they did it well—ponies, milk, and good mutton never failed us—but the entire cost fell upon the unfortunate inhabitants.

We travelled twenty-one miles next day to the village of Baba Tangi through a narrow but pleasing valley whose monotonous brown slopes would suddenly become aflame with the bright copper of a patch of dwarf willow. Near Baba Tangi, a large village, the river flows through a rocky gorge narrow enough to be bridged by a few logs. Like all the villages of the upper Oxus it lies on the flank of an alluvial fan, but unlike most of the rivers which feed these fans this one descends abruptly from a nearby glacier above which rises a very noble mountain of some 20,000 ft. Although we were not allowed by our escort to talk to anyone I tried without success to learn the name of this Hindu Kush peak.

Early in the afternoon though it was, I should not have minded stopping here if only to worship metaphorically at the foot of this fine mountain, but the escort, desirous of emulating the speed of the Sarhad courier, talked of pushing on to Kila Panja twenty miles away. Two miles farther on they thought better of it and pulled up at a very squalid village, vowing that there was no other within reach. As usual a sheep was slaughtered and poor and dirty though this place was its mutton was superbly succulent. As I ate I thought of Manning's description of Phari Dzong, that notoriously dirty Tibetan town on the road to Everest: 'Dirt, dust, grease, smoke, misery, but good mutton.'

Next morning after only two hours' marching I was not in the least surprised to come upon a much more pleasing village where we could have stopped, but it would have needed more than a trifle like that to disturb the calm, placid, unruffled impudence of our two ruffians. They laughed it off shamelessly, not even feigning to be astonished at the existence of this village. The road now left the river to climb steeply for a thousand feet before descending gradually to meet the river again at its junction with the Pamir river. Yet another thousand feet above the track smooth glacier-polished slabs of red granite glistened in the sun. At the junction we met a standing patrol of two soldiers which was apparently posted here to watch the river, at this point the Afghan-Russian frontier. Here the river-bed is some two miles wide with willow jungle, sand-banks, and islands, while the water flows in several easily forded channels between the numerous sand-banks.

The Pamir river, coming down from the Great Pamir and Victoria Lake, appeared slightly less in volume than the Ab-i-Wakhan and the valley did not have the appearance of being the main valley. At the Bozai Gumbaz junction I had thought that a traveller might be in doubt as to which valley was the main one, but here it seemed that there was little room for mistake. Wood himself when faced with this question, having to make up his mind which of the two valleys to follow, wrote: 'To my eye the stream of Sarhad (Ab-i-Wakhan) appeared the larger, but the Wakhanis held a different opinion.' As Lord Curzon tartly observes: 'Had he followed his eye instead of his guides the true source of the Oxus might have been determined half a century earlier and the two governments of Great Britain and Russia might have been spared the long controversy over the ignorant agreement.'

While the men-of-war chatted with our escort I added one more to my list of memorable bathes and afforded them fresh matter for conversation. In summer the river spreads over the whole bed and here, beside the track, the receding water had left behind it a series of very deep, clear blue pools. A rock ten feet high was my springboard from which more than once I revelled in 'the cool silver shock of the plunge in a pool's living water'. A few miles below the junction is Kila Panja, a big wide-spreading village with an old castle and a more modern mud-walled fort in the usual Asiatic style covering nearly two acres of ground. But of much more interest was the view across the river to Russia where I was astonished to see a lorry travelling along a road and followed a little later by another with a huge trailer. What appeared to be the continuation of this road could be seen as a faint straight trace along the hillside up the valley of the Pamir which, above the junction, rises fairly sharply.

If the sight of a horse makes the traveller lame, what must a lorry do? I was a little put out to find that civilization* had penetrated to

---

*   'Transportation is Civilization.' Vide Kipling's *With the Night Mail*.

Valley leading to Wakhjir pass—Tigur-man Su and Soviet frontier on hills to the left

Ascent to the Wakhjir

Lake near summit of Wakhjir pass which shows over left corner of lake

The boulder marking the Chinese-Afghan frontier on top of pass

Source of the Oxus—the black ice cave at the snout of the glacier from which it emerges can be seen in centre

Group of 'gumbaz' ten miles below Oxus source

Beginning of gorge below Bozai Gumbaz

Bozai Gumbaz plain at junction of Little Pamir and Ab-i-Wakham rivers

the upper Oxus, but I should not have scorned the offer of a lift to Ishkashim had its blessings embraced both banks of that river. On the Russian side there were two or three small villages each with an imposing looking white building which I imagined must be the H.Q. of the local O.G.P.U.—or possibly the jail or hospital, two necessary adjuncts in the advance of civilization.

In the night a furious gale blew which left behind it a thick pall of dust haze hanging low over the valley. On the other bank trucks were astir early and even at night the citizens over there seemed to gad about. Lying in my tent I frequently heard the 'revving' of an engine in low gear, and it was a mortifying reflection to think that which ever way I travelled on my side of the river, several weeks of marching would elapse before I should be able to avail myself of a lorry.

A few miles lower down we crossed two vast gravel fans. The fan is a sort of convex delta formed by the deposit of stones, gravel, and sand brought down by the torrent rushing through a narrow ravine. From its apex at the mouth of the ravine the surface of the broadly convex cone of debris is scored with water channels spread out like the ribs of a fan, so that the crossing of a large one is a troublesome business. One mounts steadily over the loose, rough surface, crossing one shallow water course after the other, expecting every minute to arrive at the summit of the slope, only to be disappointed as new sections of the cone intervene until at last the central rib is reached and the process is repeated down the other side. Cultivation is usually found tucked away between the edge of the fan and the hillside adjacent to the ravine. Between the nallahs and their respective fans, which may be five or ten miles apart, there are, of course, no villages. The intervening space may be either arid, stony waste or salt flats with a strong growth of wiry grass. There are many signs of old moraines and in the river at one place there was a high island which was probably part of an old moraine cut off by the river.

Having crossed these we marched for a brief space alongside the river, now confined in a narrow channel barely fifty yards across, while the motor road ran close along the other bank. At midday while we were changing ponies a storm of wind and dust developed and raged for two hours. This cleared the air, the sun came out, and as I looked back I could see the great snow mountain, marked on our maps as

23,000 ft., a few miles north-west of Kila Panja on the Russian side in the Shakhdara range. In a report on Russian post-war climbing activity it is stated that in 1946 a party climbed this, the highest peak of the Shakhdara range, to which they attributed a height of 7000 metres, and gave the name of 'Karl Marx'. The giving of personal names to mountains is usually a mistake. Fame is often ephemeral, the mountain is always the same. Perhaps the patron saint of revolutionary communism is worthy of commemoration, and I can think of several ways in which it might be done, but a more unfitting memorial than a great mountain to a malignant little man it would be hard to imagine.

That night at Pigish I pitched my tent in an apricot orchard. These were the first fruit trees I had seen in Wakhan, for we were now for the first time below 9000 ft., but the trees were poor and stunted. Pigish lies so close under a spur of the Hindu Kush that the October sun does not reach it until nine o'clock. Only at this comparatively late hour did we feel it warm enough to start. The next village was even worse off, for at ten o'clock when we rode through it was still in shadow, the grass white with frost and ice on the water furrows. Here the fields of short-stemmed wheat, less than a foot high, were still unreaped. In most villages, however, threshing was in full swing with mixed teams of six, eight, or even ten bullocks and donkeys tramping in a circle on the threshing-floor from dawn till dusk. The man or boy, who walks behind driving them round, carries a large wicker spoon in which to catch the droppings.

Beyond Warup where we halted for lunch the motor-road and the penitential way ran for some miles within 200 yards of each other, separated only by the river which in one place, from bank to bank, was barely forty yards across. It was an easy place to bridge, but there was, of course, none as there seems to be no intercourse whatever between the peoples on either side. It seems a pity that so unnatural a boundary as a river should be adopted as a frontier since the people of a valley are essentially a unit. A watershed is the obvious frontier, and heaven knows there are enough of them in these parts. If the Hindu Kush had to be ruled out as bringing two mighty opposites into actual contact there was the Shakhdara range and its continuation the Great Pamir.

I had already counted ten lorries that day, but here where the two roads ran side by side we met none. I was not sorry since it might have worried the Russians had they seen a Wakhi walking along dressed in khaki shorts and carrying an ice-axe. Ten lorries a day may not seem to be an extravagant use of transport, but I would have been interested to learn what they carried, for superficially the Russian side appeared more poverty-stricken than the Wakhan. The villages were fewer and smaller. The arable land, too, was less extensive, as in general the Oxus hugs the north side of the valley. Moreover, the side nallahs on which cultivation depends were deep-cut, short, and less generous, for there are few glaciers on that side and the mountains wore their snow covering with an air of unusualness. On the south side the nallahs are longer, and up them one could sometimes catch glimpses of true snow mountains, upon which the snow lay with the assurance of eternity, untouched by time or season. To see these fine mountains almost hidden from the sight of man, unnamed, never visited, seemed a prodigal waste of beauty; their sole, unconscious purpose was to provide water enough to grow wheat to keep, perhaps, 500 Wakhi families rather unnecessarily alive.

We camped six miles beyond Warup. It was now 10 October, we had left Sarhad on the 5th, and according to my map which terminated here, Ishkashim was still twenty-four miles away. For the last two days we had been told that it was 'nazdik', which in India, as I well knew, is an elastic term meaning anything from a hundred yards to five miles; but in Wakhan I found its elasticity boundless, or at any rate stretching to fifty miles, which the Sarhad courier, no doubt, would regard as a short day. At three in the afternoon we reached a large and very delightful village on a fertile flat watered by a laughing amber torrent; there were many tall poplars and shady willows, while on a cliff overlooking brook and village was a sort of grotto decorated with flags which served as a mosque. I made sure this was Ishkashim though I could see nothing which looked worthy to house a Commissar or his satellites. I began making anxious inquiries for I was in a feverish and, as it turned out, a foolish haste to meet this gentleman upon whom our immediate future seemed largely to depend. But our escort advised me to relax since Ishkashim was still some way off.

CHAPTER XVI

ISHKASHIM—CLOSE ARREST

ISHKASHIM LIES TWO OR THREE MILES back from the Oxus and at this point the river begins its great bend to the north. To reach it from this village of Qazi Deh, where we now were, the road crosses an intervening shoulder before descending to the wide Ishkashim valley formed by a stream which comes down from Shad Ishtragh, a 19,000 ft. peak on the Chitral border about fifteen miles away. Ishkashim marks the eastern extremity of Badakshan and the beginning of Wakhan of which it is the administrative centre. On one side of the stream is the small village whose extensive terraced fields fall away to the Oxus, while on the other is the official quarter—'Whitehall'—comprising the usual mud-walled fort and barracks and the unpretentious private residence of the Commissar where all business is transacted.

We reached the village at five o'clock. There was not the bazaar which I had expected the principal place of Wakhan might possess, and all the people were out in the fields cutting and carrying the harvest. Our escort halted at the stream to button their collars and tidy themselves so that their presence would be slightly less displeasing to the Commissar whom they seemed to hold in considerable respect. Neither Yusuf nor I troubled to preen our draggled feathers or even to wash, a formality which I had observed as recently as three days ago when I had bathed at Kila Panja; travel-stained, hard-used, poor but honest men who had once known better days, and now worthy of compassion, seemed to be our best line.

A sentry with some pretension to smartness stood at the gate of the high-walled compound of the Commissar's house. Nearby was gathered a small crowd of idlers, petitioners, and the tethered horses of visitors. We were told brusquely to wait, but after a bit I was led into the compound through a small garden surrounded by flower-beds and the veranda of the living-quarters, and then into another walled garden with more flower-beds, in the middle of which was an oval cemented

dais about three feet high on which some half-dozen Afghans squatted
on carpets. Mindful of the Chinese precept, 'When you bow, bow low',
I paid my ample respects, whereupon I was invited to climb up on to
the dais. Tea was being served in very small cups, a hubble-bubble was
being passed round, while a packet of American cigarettes lay on the
carpet. I filled my own pipe from my last tin and generously offered the
Commissar a cigarette from my last packet. I had no difficulty in picking
him out. He was a short, thick-set man about thirty-five years old, wearing a blue turban and a handsome embroidered white 'chapkan' which
failed to conceal a Napoleonic paunch. His full features, too, were not
unlike Napoleon's, had that great man affected a Hitler moustache.

Whether this was a garden party, a reception committee assembled on my behalf, or an official conference, I could not tell. Conversation between us was practically impossible, and had it been possible I
could think of no topic which would be suited to or explanatory of my
presence at this gathering, whether it was a garden party or, as seemed
more probable, a court-martial. Willing to please I produced my passport, half hoping that one of the many visa stamps it contained might
be mistaken for an Afghan one. It was examined curiously but it failed
to produce any general expression of respect or benevolence, and when
it finally reached a scowling sour-faced man, whom I was presently to
discover was the Chief of Police, he began comparing the photograph
with its purported original then sitting opposite to him smoking a
pipe. As became his office his suspicions were at once aroused. This
was not surprising considering that I was now wearing a beard, that
the photograph had been taken before the war, and that he was looking at it upside down. Bacon tells us that there is nothing makes a man
suspect much, more than to know little. This man, I was to find, was a
most dangerous combination of abysmal ignorance and instantaneous
deductive power.

The atmosphere engendered by a party seated on a cement dais
at six o'clock of an October evening in Wakhan cannot be warm,
but when the Chief of Police began drawing attention to the invidi-
ous comparisons he was making it became perceptibly cooler. Yusuf
was now introduced, but since he had no passport at all and no one
could understand Turki his appearance gratified nobody except, perhaps, the Grand Inquisitor. To him we were already a couple of rather

amateurish spies upon whom his deductive talents, though they might
be exercised, could hardly be sharpened. An uncouth individual who
was suspected of talking Hindustani was then summoned. He talked in
a fast screech, so fast as to be hardly understandable even had it been
in English, but I caught a word here and there and through him tried
to convey to the court that though we were bound for Gilgit and had
been obliged by the Commissar to come so far out of our way, we bore
no malice and would be content with Chitral—at which they seemed
amused. This mangler of Hindustani was in reality a soldier, as I think
they all were, but he was in mufti and appeared to act as scullion and
purveyor of the Commissar's hubble-bubble in his spare time. Most of
the men, I found, only wore uniform when on duty, either to save wear
and tear or because there were not enough to go round.

The sun had by now sunk. The Commissar rose, turned to the west,
spread his carpet, and began his evening prayer. One or two of the
more devout fell in behind him to follow suit while the rest continued
to smoke and chat. This done the Commissar stood up and delivered a
long harangue in a stern military manner directed mainly at the Grand
Inquisitor. This, as we soon learnt, was our sentence and his orders,
but I was yet unaware of this and when the meeting broke up I walked
out through the compound and began to look about for a place where
I could pitch my tent. The Chief of Police who was behind motioned
me on. I followed him into another walled compound a little way off,
lined on one side with a series of small rooms. It was dirty, and some
lime strewn over an excavation in the middle was unpleasantly suggestive of wholesale executions and mass graves. It was not at all the sort
of place I should have chosen for a camp site, but that was not the idea.
At the door of one of these cells, for so they were, the Chief of Police
suddenly turned on me and thrust both hands into the pockets of my
windproof. I started to hand him off but I soon found a couple of soldiers, one in front and one behind, threatening me with fixed bayonets. Having gone through the upper pockets he signed to me to take
off my trousers. This I refused to do. Someone then suggested it would
be better done indoors so we were bundled into one of the rooms followed by the policeman and a couple of assistants.

This mud-walled room, although only about ten feet square, was
not without amenities. There were a couple of chairs and half the earth

floor was covered with a carpet. Yusuf and I were put on the chairs while the search party ranged themselves opposite on the carpet. All our kit—the two pony loads—was brought in and thrown on the floor between us; but before starting on this I had still to be properly 'frisked'. Accordingly I handed over my windproof trousers. These were of double thickness so the ends were slit and a search made for sewn-in papers. At last the stage was set for the big scene. My rucksack and kit-bag were unceremonously up-ended and a pyramid of miscellaneous articles rose in front of the Grand Inquisitor. His scowl rested lovingly on this wealth of material—each piece a clue in some grotesque chain of reasoning—and he metaphorically rubbed his hands at the happy chance which had provided him with a long night's work of inquisitiveness. As for me I was wellnigh gibbering with the indignation I was unable to express at this high-handed business and the rough treatment bestowed on my precious possessions.

One assistant, having first satisfied his own curiosity, handed each article to his superior, while the other, armed with paper and pen, made an inventory. Pieces of clothing were scrutinized, felt, and thrown in one corner without comment, but I was fiercely challenged to explain by demonstration the significance of a silk scarf and a hair-brush. Then they found the money, of which I had a considerable amount in single rupee notes and coin and Chinese paper dollars—the latter of no great intrinsic value but useful for spills. All had to be laboriously counted, note by note, anna by anna, so that by the time that was done my indignation had cooled and I had taken to making sarcastic suggestions which, though they were not understood, were not liked. Then came a packet of 'Bromo'. This baffled them, but that too was counted leaf by leaf until at length arithmetic failed and I helpfully supplied the answer as printed on the packet. Camera and films, of which I had about twenty exposed and a few unexposed, excited less joy than I had feared. They wanted to open a few of the films to see what was inside, but I managed to express such convincing consternation that they surprisingly desisted. Then came the find of the evening—a photo-electric exposure meter. The Grand Inquisitor's eyes fairly sparkled with satisfaction. 'Telegram' he almost yelled in his excitement, meaning apparently that it was some cunning wireless gadget for sending messages, and a soldier was immediately dispatched with it to the Commissar.

Solid 'Meta' fuel puzzled them, but after I had failed to persuade them to eat some I had to demonstrate its use by lighting it. Maps, photographs, books, excited almost as much interest as the 'telegram' and each was carefully examined every way up but the right one. The double bottom of my kit-bag was slit open, every seam of my sleeping-bag felt, and finally the tent turned inside out. It would have puzzled a conjuror to conceal anything from these hawks. Nevertheless, when the search was finished the Grand Inquisitor coolly asked me where were my pistol and binoculars.

Yusuf's gear was then overhauled and I was surprised at the oddities my companion in misery saw fit to carry, most of it presumably for trade—many embroidered Turki caps, copper tea-pots, a pair of new riding boots, yards of cloth, atta, a bag of bread hard as rock, some 'kurut', and numerous little packages of queer-looking powders, pills, bark, whose use the Afghans seemed to comprehend perfectly. It was now getting on for 11 p.m. The search had lasted for some four hours, so that I rejoiced to see a large tray of food brought in. 'All sorrows are alleviated by eating bread', but here we had a very rich mutton stew and a large bowl of yoghourt which they called 'mos'. Yusuf, overwhelmed by this last turn in our misfortunes, was now sobbing quietly to himself and would not eat. Loud challenges and slapping of butts outside heralded the arrival of the Commissar and the return of my exposure-meter which he now handed back. I had already noticed a single wire mounted on poplar poles near the Commissar's house, and it was the telephone operator, the local expert on Western gadgets, who had been asked to decide the significance of the exposure-meter. I learnt later that this line was connected to Faizabad 100 miles north-west.

The Commissar gravely surveyed my belongings littering the floor like the wares of a junk shop, and while the Inquisitor handed him everything which he considered compromising or dangerous, such as maps, compass, books, diaries, papers, passport, photos, pencils, my pocket-knife and ice-axe and Yusuf's sheath-knife, I was bidden to pack the rest. This gave me the opportunity of spiriting away the camera and films. The only light came from a cracked 'Dietz' lantern, so that it would have been equally easy for the Inquisitor or his assistants to spirit away a few rupees, but as far as I could tell not an anna stuck to their fingers. Before leaving us to digest our sorrows they told us that there were two sentries by the door and that if we wanted to go outside during the night we must knock on the door which was unlocked—failure to do this would have fatal results.

Next day, except for two soldier servants who brought our meals from the Commissar's own mess, no one came near us. The food bore out the promise of the Commissar's paunch. He was no ascetic. He liked rich food and plenty of it, and a capable cook saw that he got it. For breakfast we had bread, fresh butter, a plateful of sugar in lieu of jam, and pale scented tea. For lunch and supper the changes were rung, not too frequently, on spicy pilaus, rich stews, fish from the Oxus, and always a liberal helping of yoghourt as a corrective. Yusuf did not fare quite so well for his meals were brought from the guard-room.

Even so between these welcome gastronomic landmarks there were many long hours to contemplate the helpless degradation of captivity, our complete subjection to the will of this taciturn, suspicious Commissar and his armed blackguards outside, and our problematic future. There was nothing to read and nothing to do except stare through the open door at the officious sentry outside who stared back at us. The guards, who lived within the compound, carried out their sanitary duties under the compound wall and thither we had to go but always attended by the sentry who all the time stood over us. How I came to hate him.

Yusuf was in a poor way. As well as having collapsed morally he now had fever and spent the day huddled out of sight under his 'poshteen', groaning, sighing deeply, and occasionally poking his head out to spit. As a companion in misery he was an unqualified success and I began to eye him with almost as much loathing as I did the sentries. It has long been remarked that we hate those whom we have wronged more than those who have wronged us, and though I might think I had not done Yusuf any harm it was quite clear that I had not done him any good. He had trusted himself blindly to me and for that he was now languishing as a suspected spy in an Afghan jail, 400 miles from his home, further from his destination than when he started, sick, without medicine, and his horse (which he regarded with the affection Sancho bestowed on his ass 'Dapple') tethered outside uncared for, at the mercy of the first Afghan horse-thief who should come along.

Instead of travelling respectably and respected under the aegis of a sahib who, he thought, would no doubt be received everywhere with deference, he was lying in a mud cell, watched by an armed man, in company with the same sahib who was himself being treated with as much respect as a Kashgar donkey-boy.

Whenever the servants brought a meal I asked to see the Commissar, for my uncertainty as to his intentions was my chief worry, so after breakfast the following day, as this request was still ignored, I determined upon a hunger-strike. It was the only weapon I had; it had been used effectively by many more distinguished prisoners, and though their denial of their prison fare (skilly?) undoubtedly called for less strength of mind than I should have to exercise to deny myself pilau, mutton, and yoghourt, I felt sufficient sullen dogged resentment against the Commissar to throw his food in his face if I got the chance.

At lunch time then, instead of starting up with shameless eagerness I just lay still, averting my eyes from savoury temptation and calmly waving it away. At first they thought I must be ill, then they asked if there was anything wrong with the food, and when I had made them understand that I was resolved not to eat any more of the Commissar's food until I had seen him, their consternation and concern were most gratifying. The sentry came in to see what was the matter, followed shortly by the whole of the guard—about a dozen of them— who quite filled the room as they expostulated excitedly. Word of this ominous turn on the part of the worm was sent to the Commissar and the answer came back that he would see me after I had finished lunch. This was no good. Another messenger went and returned to say the Commissar was a busy man but that he would see me some time. I steeled myself for at least another forty-eight hours' fasting, for he did not seem to me a man sensitive to the suffering of others, and meanwhile I made some tea from our own small store on a Primus stove since I was more anxious to mortify the Commissar than myself. But within half an hour an orderly came to say that he would see me at once, and forthwith I was conducted to the house, into the first garden where the living quarters were.

The Commissar was indeed a busy man. Surrounded by a few choice friends, my particular enemy the Chief of Police among them, he was reclining on a divan smoking a hookah, killing time with a pack of cards. The Chief of Police occupied himself mending a mandoline and occasionally bent his powerful mind to helping the Commissar cheat at Patience, while the Secretary read aloud a thundering leader from the 'Kabul Clarion'. Presently they started a round of Afghan 'Nap' in which I joined.

They were friendly enough and it was an amusing afternoon. But it was one from which I got little satisfaction. A few puffs at the hookah (not an easy smoke for a beginner) and a bland promise that we must remain at least five days or until orders came for our disposal was the sum total. This, I thought, meant just what I had feared—Kabul, and five days more confinement before we even set out for a place which for all I knew might be a month's journey away. Before I was conducted back to our cell the Commissar gave me the pack of cards—greasy, thumbed, torn. I remember it still. The two of clubs was missing and the queen of spades had lost her head, but I think that that pack saved me losing mine. I am no card player, but now I played Patience from morning until it was too dark to see, and when the servants brought the meals we used to have a quick whist drive. The Afghans, by the way, deal and play in the opposite direction to us. Apart from this reason-saving concession our treatment was as rigorous as ever. Except for necessity we could not stir from the cell, and once when I tried to sit on the doorstep in the sun—for it was cold inside—a fierce altercation with the sentry ensued. He ended it in his own favour by loading and cocking his rifle. Yusuf implored me to come in and at this I did so, for I never knew quite how far one could go with these uncouth Yahoos.

There was an unexpected and pleasing development next day. About 10 a.m., comparatively early for the Commissar, I was summoned once more to the garden where I found him sitting at a table drinking tea in company with a young smiling, shifty-looking man, dressed in an elegant 'chapkan', who addressed me first in fluent Hindustani and then startled me by switching suddenly to very good English. He was a man of many tongues, and of guile, too, as I later found. He tried several more of them on me, including Russian, but, of course, got no response; and I soon discovered that he had been sent for by the Commissar for a purpose which presently appeared. After asking me what I thought he was and receiving the correct reply—an

Afghan army officer (for it was a safe bet that most educated Afghans were that)—he acknowledged with a smirk of satisfaction that he was a lieutenant. I was told later that he was below commissioned rank, and from some financial transactions I had with him subsequently I formed the opinion that he should have been below any rank at all.

Having drunk tea we got down to business. The Commissar produced a formidable wad of paper, the sheets of which he folded down the middle lengthwise. On one side he wrote a question in Persian, to which, when it had been translated by the shifty scholar, I had to write the answer in English and sign it. The questions were ingenious and cunningly devised to bring out all my past history and background, and since I had nothing to conceal I began giving it them. However, as soon as they learnt I had been in the army during the war they had something to work on and I began to see that in their eyes a British officer in Wakhan was *ipso facto* a spy. So, while telling the truth, I deemed it advisable to suppress one or two facts, such as, for instance, that long ago until I had thought better of it I had been a professional soldier. This involved me in writing a treatise on the selection and promotion of British officers in war-time, the status of reserve officers, and kindred subjects. Nor did it seem necessary to tell everything about the last war, for in their vivid imaginations the word 'parachutist' would have at once conjured up visions of furtive but dare-devil activity in hostile country. This was by no means my cup of tea, but the knowledge would have made them suspect the more that I was now following my old vocation in their country.

A long morning's work only whetted the Commissar's thirst for knowledge and he had hardly approached the main question of why I was in what he was pleased to think was the very important strategic frontier district of Wakhan. I was warned to attend at the same time next day.

All criminals know, or should know, that it is most unwise to volunteer either information or opinions, or even to make any remarks except, perhaps, about the weather, in the presence of one's accusers. Before we continued this game of 'Consequences' there was some chat about the late war and its politics from which I gathered that the Commissar was soaked in Russian propaganda. He repeated the familiar point that the Russians had suffered fifteen million casualties, the

British Empire half a million, ergo the Russians had fought and won the war almost unaided. My answer, that it merely showed bad tactics and generalship and a reckless disregard for human life, was not well received. The recent attainment of independence by India and Pakistan was then referred to, and not wishing to waste an opportunity of showing him how foolish his suspicions were, I airily remarked that however great the importance of the Wakhan frontier may have been to the British before, it was of less than none now that we had left India for good. Ten hours later, when I was still being examined, a garbled version of this was to recoil on my own head.

It was naturally difficult to convince two such men that I had come to Wakhan simply and solely for my own pleasure. Many of these Afghan officers had had their military education in Turkey and it is, I think, a Turkish proverb which says that all travel is a foretaste of hell. That anyone should wish to see the source of the Oxus or the Hindu Kush was to them the flimsiest of pretexts. Having been posted here willy-nilly so far from the delights of Kabul the Commissar was determined not to go any farther—I doubt if he ever left his compound; and the shifty scholar reluctantly confessed that once he had been obliged to go as far as Kila Panja; so that to ask them to believe that I travelled purely for the sake of travelling was too much.

Where, when, and why, therefore, had I first conceived the idea of coming to Wakhan? Had I left England with that intention? Where had I been and what had I done since arriving in India? And what had I seen in Wakhan that was of military or political importance? To answer the last was, I thought, extremely simple, and at the risk of offending the *amour propre* of the Commissar, the governor of that important territory, I replied that while I was extremely ignorant of such matters and no more a judge of military and political questions than they would be of beer, I could answer in one word—nothing. Finally, my maps—why did I have a map showing part of Wakhan? And the possession of this, I found, was thought to be as incriminating for me as the possession of a jemmy would be to a man accused of loitering with intent. It was useless to point out that the map in question showed also parts of India, China, and Russia, for they seemed to think that since they had no map of Wakhan and did not know that one existed, I must have obtained it from some very secret source and that whoever compiled it had no right to include the strategically important Wakhan.

The session continued all day, with a break for lunch, until eleven o'clock at night, by which time we were sitting on rugs in the Commissar's house eating apples and pears after an uncommonly good dinner. While I wrote the Commissar played Patience, but his mind was evidently on his next question rather than the game, for we had frequently to point out opportunities of moving a card which he had overlooked. Occasionally, he executed a few soulful strophes on the mandoline. There were two other breaks while he said his prayers, first at sundown and then again after supper. In almost the final question my voluntary remark of the morning was turned in exactly the opposite sense and used against me, for the Commissar seemed to have more than an inkling of trial procedure as carried out at Moscow, the last syllable of which, by the way, he always pronounced to rhyme with the domestic animal. If I thought, the question ran, that Wakhan was of no military importance why had I said that morning that it was of great importance to the British. The shifty scholar would not admit having mistranslated and since the Commissar insisted on having an answer I merely wrote that it was a waste of time answering stupid questions. All three of us were getting tired of playing 'Consequences' but I imagine the Commissar was compiling this precious document more for the benefit of his superiors at Kabul than for his own pleasure and wished to impress them with his acumen and thoroughness. Before leaving them I asked for some assurance that we should start for Chitral on the fifth day as promised, to which he assented with the saving remark, 'Insh Allah'.

On returning to the cell I found Yusuf had been removed elsewhere in order to prevent any collusion prior to his cross-examination. The pseudo-lieutenant could speak Turki too; and we later met several officers who were able to converse a little with Yusuf with the help of the Turkish they had picked up when attending military schools in Turkey. In the afternoon Yusuf rejoined me, his examination, of course, having produced nothing, and with him came Ghulam Moxd, our shifty interpreter. He was becoming quite affectionate towards me and the mere fact that he spoke English was enough to make me grateful to him. He now assured me that the 'Chief' as they called the Commissar (who was

Peak (*c.* 20,000 ft.) of Hindu Kush
above Baba Tangi

Islands in Oxus below Kila Panja

The Oxus below Warup

The Oxus and Russian motor-road

In the Sarhad gorge
above Sarhad

Sarhad and Oxus—mouth of gorge in
centre

Captivity—Yusuf at Ishkashim

Yusuf in a fit of despair

in fact a Colonel in the army) would send us off next day to Chitral by way of the Sanglich valley which, he said, was three or four days' journey away. I would be well advised to have some Afghan money for the journey, and since the Afghan rupee (the 'Afghani') was the equivalent of an Indian rupee the exchange was simple. Whereupon I changed twenty rupees with him and also relieved him of a nice 'chapkan' he had brought to sell, the price of which, he said, was eighty 'Afghanis'. For this I handed over eighty Indian rupees.

Bright and early next morning he came with a final quittance for me to sign by which I acknowledged the return of all my money, papers, and belongings. I had not got back any maps, papers, or diaries yet, but an escort would conduct us as far as the frontier and there hand them over. This sounded reasonable and I was too pleased at the thought of getting away to haggle over terms. The Commissar, looking me straight in the face and solemnly shaking hands on it, had assured me that he was satisfied of my innocent motives and that he would see we got to Chitral. Ghulam, too, protested that the Chief was a man of his word and that everything would be done as he said. Yusuf and I had had our loads ready since dawn, Yusuf having donned his new riding boots for the occasion and thrown the old pair away. But as the morning wore on and nothing happened our mood quickly passed from impatience to desperate hope, and by afternoon had reached utter despondency.

At last at five o'clock, when we had given up hope and when the first gusts of a brewing dust-storm were shaking the tall poplars, we were summoned to the Commissar's compound. The escort of four soldiers was waiting. All four were dressed regardless of expense in uniform, with greatcoats and belts, and armed with rifles and bayonets. The Commissar had ready a sealed package containing my papers, which he delivered to the senior soldier together with a long harangue. Ghulam, as if deeply impressed with the Commissar's benevolence and my exceptional good fortune, explained that the gist of this was that we were no longer to be treated as prisoners, that the escort was merely a safe conduct, Badakshan being a wild country, where the inhabitants were totally opposed to strangers. My papers, pocket-knife, and ice-axe, now in possession of the escort, would all be handed back at the frontier, and I dwelt with fond anticipation upon the delightful ceremony presently to be conducted on some high pass, near some Afghan boundary stone on which I should spit, while the bodyguard, saluting respectfully, would lay our belongings reverently at our feet and bid us a long farewell.

The dust cut short our mutual expressions of esteem, regret, and farewell. I shook them warmly and almost gratefully by the hand, little realising that both were liars and one a swindler.

CHAPTER XVII

DESTINATION UNKNOWN

FROM ISHKASHIM THE TRACK at once began climbing gradually in a south-westerly direction to a low pass (the Sardab), with the telephone line running alongside it. We had not gone half a mile in the gathering gloom of the dust-storm before I learnt that, instead of being safely escorted, we were being closely guarded, for when I attempted to take a short-cut across a bend in the track I was immediately driven back with threats and imprecations. The soldier in charge of our party, who had stayed behind to collect a horse, now rode up carrying my documents tied up in a blanket. It occurred to me that I ought to have checked these before leaving. Apart from my diaries, which I valued, I was concerned about my passport, for without it I should look uncommonly foolish on my arrival in India. I therefore asked to be allowed to see the papers. When this was refused with a snarl I signified that either I would not go on until I was satisfied or else that I would go back. The whole escort immediately clustered round, shouting and pushing, whereupon I had recourse to my Sarhad tactics of a sit-down strike. But these soldiers were of sterner stuff than the police. The three on foot whipped out their bayonets while the man on the horse, not wishing to inconvenience himself, cocked his rifle. I got up and went on, reviling them loudly but uselessly, for I had not the courage to push provocation to extremes, in order to find out how far they would go. My friend the Commissar might even have hoped for some such outcome, and I could well imagine his official report of the regrettable incident: 'The Commissar regrets that the Englishman was unfortunately shot while resisting his escort.'

This was a bad start to a bad journey. By nightfall, having lost the man with the baggage pony, we were stumbling about the narrow ways of a village on the other side of the pass. Having pushed our way into several courtyards we were at length led into a narrow whitewashed room, which with its thick walls and niches reminded me of a private chapel. It was lit by resinous slips of willow about two feet long placed horizontally in holes in the wall. An hour later the baggage turned up, the door was locked, and our four blackguards made themselves comfortable alongside us. To show my dislike of their company I turned in without joining in their meal, but I found they were not so sensitive to slights on their hospitality as was the Commissar.

It was a sparkling, frosty autumn morning, the blue smoke from the stirring villages curling lazily in the still air, as once more we took to the road and headed south-west down an open grassy valley—such a morning that for a time I forgot my resentment against the four chattering hooligans behind me. In two days, or at most three, we should be rid of them and their likes for good. Freed now from any control, they had exerted the authority conferred by their uniforms and rifles to procure themselves mounts. One rode on top of my baggage while the other two rode double. Badakshan is a country of horses—few people walk—and its horses are much sought after both in Gilgit and in Chitral for polo. Yusuf was always pressing me to ride his nag, partly out of kindness and partly because for prudence sake he had long since given out that the horse was mine. But with his new boots and his continuing fever he was in no shape for walking.

After six or seven miles the valley debouched on to wide flats where its small stream joined a fine, fast-flowing river coming down from higher mountains away to the south. I felt sure that up that river lay the way to our pass into Chitral, and it was therefore with surprise and some disappointment that at the junction we turned off to follow the combined streams into a gorge running west. Apart from some superb rock scenery this gorge and the road through it were as wearisome and as long as most. Except for a small village close to the entrance there was nothing until we reached another (Tirguran) eleven miles farther down. I was troubled by the direction of the gorge, which tended to edge away rather north of west. It was easy enough to tell our general direction, but I had no map and not the shadow of an idea about the geography of Afghanistan. Kabul, I thought vaguely, must lie to the west and Chitral to the south. Any course therefore that was not south of west would be unlikely to lead to Chitral, unless the boundary shot out to the north in the erratic and unexpected way that boundaries sometimes do.

We had covered about twenty-three miles before we stopped at the rest-house of Tirguran. In Badakshan all villages have these square single rooms. There is a raised earth platform for sleeping running round the walls, and in the middle of the floor is a circular fireplace sunk in the ground. The merits of this type of fireplace are that no one can see it and only about two people can get near enough to appreciate it. Even the boiling of a pot is a difficult operation—only possible by first kindling a great conflagration and then making use of the resulting ashes. At these places all travellers are welcome and as our party was of transcendent interest 'House-Full' notices were up very soon after our arrival. The soldiers were regarded with a respectful attention which, though perhaps deemed necessary in the interests of prudence, was unworthy of the honest peasants who bestowed it, quite unmerited by the recipients, and sickening to an observer such as myself. I was beginning to hate the sight of a uniform. At the social evenings in these rest-houses our senior soldier was listened to with deference and the wag of the party with sycophantic applause; and although any attempt at conversation between us and the villagers was strictly forbidden, there was, of course, no embargo on their discussing us.

It was not until eleven o'clock that we got our relay of ponies, so we started off going as fast as I could walk to make up for lost time. We had another twenty-two mile march to do before reaching what our mendacious guard informed us would be Sanglich, at the foot of the pass to Chitral. We crossed the river (here the Warduj, later the Kokcha) to the left bank by a bridge over a narrow cleft, and twelve miles on halted to change ponies at a pleasant village (Sufian), where the persistent walls of the gorge at length began to give ground. I had been troubled yesterday by our line of march but to-day I began to feel more than anxious. At every twist of the gorge—and there were many—I hoped and expected to see the river break back southwards. Indeed, it seemed eager to do this, but round each corner there was always some spiteful buttress of rock to thrust it farther away, so that from west our direction became north-west, and then for the last ten miles due north. We walked wearily up the last fan to where the so-called Sanglich (in reality Chakaran) stood in its russet and vermilion-leaved apricot orchards. Night fell, the stars of the Plough appeared one by one, until the Pointers confirmed too surely our unpromising course and shattered a wild hope I had that the sun had somehow gone astray.

Besides a supper of bread and a thin 'goulash', in the morning the rest-house provided tea and bread to speed the wayfarers on their road. This came in waves like a flowing tide. The first intimation that the tide was making would be the arrival of the headman himself carrying a copper-pot of tea and some flat round loaves; a few minutes later another greybeard* would totter in with a similar contribution; then a boy with his and a trayful of small China bowls, then more and more until the whole place was awash with bowls, and teapots, and bread. Anyone could join this tea-fight. In addition to the bona fide travellers and those who brought the breakfast, most of the village elders and certainly all the village idlers muscled in on this gratuitous pipe-opener and broke the back of the morning with tea and chat. It was a pleasant and inexpensive custom, for no one minded what he drank so long as it was hot.

Sunday 19 October was the great day when, according to the fiction assiduously sustained by our guards, we should reach the frontier, so that when a mile below Chakaran the river swung abruptly round to the west my hopes revived. Evidently, I thought, there was no pass to cross. Lower down, perhaps, the river itself would become the frontier. Some twelve miles farther on, when I saw a bridge and on the south side a broad road which disappeared into another valley running due south, I became quite excited. My annoyance and disappointment were therefore all the keener when we held steadily to our course along the north bank of the river, leaving the bridge behind us. So far we had marched at a great pace without a halt, for I was buoyed up with eager hope, but having passed the bridge and the valley leading south I sat down sullenly to eat some bread. This occasioned another scene with the senior soldier who, while the others went on, remained with me as he always did, his confounded horse almost treading on my heels. He raved, pointed his rifle, and finally cocked it. My already parched mouth became dryer with tension, but I munched away until the crust was finished, sneered at him, and went on.

---

*   'Greybeard' is a misnomer in the East where grey beards are usually dyed red with henna.

The two valleys having joined, their combined rivers (now the Kokcha) flowed north-west again through a fertile plain, where on our side were a fort, barracks, and parade ground, with a large village almost hidden by trees. Was this the frontier town with Chitral across the river? As I have admitted, my notions of the geography hereabouts were childish. I had a suspicion that the Hindu Kush must intervene somewhere, but on the other hand by the Kabul river, I knew, one could reach India without climbing a pass. But so persuaded was I that Chitral was our destination and so hateful the prospect of any other, that no hypothesis was too wild and no supposition too flimsy for me to clutch at.

As we reached the outskirts, our road met another coming from the barracks and at the corner stood a party of young men headed by a familiar figure in an elegant white 'chapkan'. It was Ghulam Moxd, the shifty scholar.

'How the devil did you get here, Ghulam?'

'Oh, by riding. Major, we have both been deceived.'

'How's that? Aren't we going to Chitral after all?'

'Oh yes, you will go to Chitral. But the Chief has deceived us both.'

'Well, when shall we get there?'

'Oh, perhaps, this evening. I have brought my friends. They want to see the Englishman who is my friend. But the Chief has deceived us both.'

'Well, I don't understand you. Damn you and your friends. I'm in a hurry to get to Chitral and can't stop. Good-bye.'

And with that I rudely left them to hurry on by a shady, dusty road, through a well-stocked bazaar where I greedily eyed piles of melons and apples, and then down to a bridge over another river flowing in from the east. On the other side of this our guard took us into a court-yard opening on to a neat bungalow, in front of which was a small ter-race and a veranda. We were left in charge of a dignified looking man with a black spade-beard, who seated us on the terrace and brought tea and fruit, while the guard departed in search of fresh horses. Presently another man, whom I took to be the village schoolmaster, joined us. He was dressed in European fashion, and though the afternoon sun beat warmly into this walled garden he wore a buttoned-up overcoat, black woollen gloves, and a black Astrakhan hat. They had evidently been forewarned, for when we questioned them as best we could we learnt that if we were lucky enough to obtain fresh horses then Chitral might be reached that night. Ghulam's reiterated refrain became even more worrying and inexplicable. Had the Commissar bilked me of my papers and passport?

Against all the rules imposed by our guard they told us that this place was Baharak. On the map it is marked as 'Khairabad' but that name is unknown locally. Mr Evert Barger, historian and archaeologist, who in the course of an expedition to northern Afghanistan in 1938 rode here from Faizabad, asserts that some ruins he found at the north end of the Baharak plain mark the site of the ancient capital of Badakshan. In a paper in the *Geographical Journal*, May 1939, the reading of which, by the way, made me feel that I had traversed Wakhan with unseeing eyes, Mr Barger argues that, contrary to accepted opinion, this southern branch of the old Silk Route which followed the Oxus valley through Wakhan was nearly as important as the northern one going from Termez on the middle Oxus, north of the Pamirs and between the Alai and Trans-Alai mountains to Kashgar. 'Wakhan', he wrote, 'is known to be full of fortifications, buildings, and caves which Sir Aurel Stein believed to be of Sassanid date, and among which he also found traces of Buddhist worship. No site in Wakhan has yet been excavated and in a sense it has never been explored. The route through Wakhan has always followed the southern bank of the Oxus, for the floor of the valley is broader there, and the chief settlements lie on the Afghan side. Sir Aurel Stein and Olufsen have explored the Russian bank, but, so far as I am aware, no record exists of any traveller who has been on the Afghan side of lower Wakhan since Wood made his famous journey to the sources of the Oxus a hundred years ago. Thorough excavation of some of the ancient sites in Wakhan must be perhaps the most important single item on any agenda of archaeological work in Central Asia...'

For once the guards seemed to have met their match; by the time they had stolen horses, or brow-beaten their owners into lending them, it was too late to start. Accustomed to soldiers living in the barracks, the people of Baharak either had a more just appreciation of their status than had the up-country hicks, or else they knew better how to out-bluster them. While our hooligans were considering this

unwonted show of spirit by the civilian rabbit, a slim, wiry man with
grey goatee beard, fierce hooked nose, and shrewd but rather wild
grey eyes rode into the courtyard. He rode on top of a couple of bush-
els of apples and was followed by a servant sitting upon two more.
Having washed ceremonially in the water channel which ran along
the terrace, he first exhorted the company and then fell to praying.
No one responded—neither Spade-beard, the Schoolmaster, the hooligans, Yusuf, his servant, nor myself—so when he had done he stood
up and delivered, *ex cathedra*, what I believed and hoped was a severe
homily on the neglect of religious duty. In extenuation I might have
told him that four at least of the company were already damned and
that no amount of prayer, I hoped, would save them from burning
in hell fire. Whether he was the owner of the villa, an itinerant fruit
broker, or a homing prophet sated with locusts and wild honey, I
never discovered. But it was all one, for he behaved as though he had
bought the place.

The whole company, including ourselves and an officer and his
servant who had ridden in at dusk, took supper in the villa, seated in a
long row against one wall with the Prophet in the place of honour on
the extreme right and myself in the place of dishonour on the extreme
left. Having dealt with the mutton stew and having seen the tea begin
circulating, Spade-beard produced a lamp and began a mysterious
game. Concealed about his person were several bundles of folded
pieces of paper which he proceeded to unfold one by one and read,
commenting occasionally on what he read to the company at large.
Whether they were ballot papers, begging letters, testimonials to his
stewardship (for that I thought he must be), or the blackmailing letters
of a 'poison-pen', is a problem which I shall never solve. The Prophet
grew restless and when Spade-beard reached for yet another bundle,
he indicated by standing up to pray that he for one had had enough.
Calmly and methodically Spade-beard continued unfolding papers,
rudely ignoring this strong hint, but the Soldier and the Schoolmaster
obediently ranged themselves in echelon behind the Prophet, while the
rest of the company signified their respect for his foibles by ceasing to
chatter. That done, all except the Schoolmaster made their beds where
they sat. But in the corner by me was a real bed about two feet high
to which the Schoolmaster strode with a resolute air like a man going

to his fate. He took one stride on to it, stood up while he replaced his black gloves with a pair of white ones, and then lay down.

We left early next morning, without a blessing from the Prophet, but encouraged by a speech in English from the Schoolmaster which he had evidently been thinking up in the long night watches—'Chitral one'—meaning, we supposed, one day's march to Chitral, thus dutifully doing his little best to support this elaborate hoax.

At the northern end of the Baharak plain there is a small village and a serai, Pa-i-Shahr (at the foot of the town), which is close to the site of the ancient city discovered by Mr Barger. From Baharak the road was wide, having evidently been recently constructed with a view to motor traffic, but below Pa-i-Shahr, road and river plunge into a narrow gorge. Here the new road has been hewn out of a solid rock face—a considerable feat of engineering, for it is wide enough to take a jeep or possibly bigger trucks. The gorge persists for eighteen barren miles with only one small half-way village, where there is a serai and a few tea-shops. We took tea here, and from this point onwards the road was alive with donkey traffic, most of it returning empty in our direction. Evidently there was a biggish town ahead, but what it was I neither knew nor cared. We were still going north-west and in spite of the Schoolmaster's reassuring words I had at last concluded that we were bound for Kabul, heaven alone knew how many marches away. An ominous sign was the telegraph line which still dogged us and which I grew to hate almost as much as I did our guard.

At length the walls of the gorge began to recede, leaving space for terraced fields, orchards, and houses to cluster in a narrow strip on either bank. At three o'clock we were on the outskirts of a town. We passed an ancient stone bridge and entered a bustling bazaar to be finally shepherded by our guard under an open archway leading into a compound. The first thing I noticed was a lorry and at once I guessed we were in Faizabad; for had not the shifty Scholar informed me with pride that from Faizabad there was a motor road to Kabul?

Lake Dufferin (Hauz-i-Dorah) near foot of Dorah pass, Afghan side

The Afghan captain at Sanglich

Yusuf and his nag on top of Dorah pass (*c.* 15,000 ft.)

The 'short blackguard' and Chitrali falconer

CHAPTER XVIII

FAIZABAD AND FREEDOM

S O WE HAD BEEN LED up the garden path after all and the meaning of Ghulam's incantation at Baharak was clear; though why he, one of the parties to the deceit, should have taken the trouble to ride ahead to confess and couple himself with me as one of the deceived I cannot imagine. It had been a well-wrought stratagem in which I could see no sense except, perhaps, as a rather cruel jest. But I admired the thoroughness with which the plot had been sustained and the way in which outsiders had entered into the spirit of the thing; for in our intercourse with the guards and in theirs with the hundreds of people we had encountered on the journey, I had not once heard the word 'Faizabad'. The talk had always been of Chitral—although we were heading in precisely the opposite direction. Which merely goes to show that all Afghans are experienced, industrious, and quite often picturesque liars.

Faizabad, the present capital of Badakshan including the district of Wakhan, has seen much worse days. In 1821 it was completely destroyed by Murad Beg, an Uzbek chieftain of superior talent and predatory habits—a man after the style of Sikander Beg the Albanian hero or Mehmed Ali of Egypt, but handicapped by a meaner and less known sphere of action than theirs. Having wiped out the town he removed the inhabitants to his capital at Kunduz a hundred miles to the west. In 1838 Wood visited him there and found it a wretched, unhealthy place built in a swamp. From there Wood proceeded to the desolate Faizabad and, having seen the ruined houses and wasted orchards of this far more eligible site, felt constrained to remark: 'It was impossible to behold the desolation of so fair a scene without commiserating the unfortunate inhabitants and execrating the tyrant, or without shuddering to think that one man should have the power to work so much mischief.'

Though Murad Beg worked on a small canvas he seems to have wrought some notable mischief in his time, but our more recent practitioners in this line would quickly exhaust a Wood's powers of shuddering. Later the Uzbeks were expelled and under Abdur Rahman (1867) Faizabad regained its former status. Now it is a considerable trading centre and the cantonment for northern Afghanistan. Situated as it is in a narrow valley, it can never at any time have supported a large population so that it probably owes its importance to its position on the Kokcha river where routes from the Oxus, Khanabad, and Wakhan converge. In 1937 a motor road to Khanabad, 135 miles away, and Kabul, was opened.

After a short wait we were taken through another and busier bazaar to the cantonment and administrative offices on a hill half a mile from the town. Unlike the Commissar's these were real government offices equipped with doubtfully efficient telephones, dry ink-stands, and nibless pens—but for the absence of empty tea-cups one might have been in Whitehall. We were set down in the Governor's office (by no means ornate or even comfortable) and presently a frightening bark from the sentry at the door announced the arrival of the Governor. He was in khaki uniform with Sam-Browne belt, breeches, gaiters, and spurs with chains, things which I had not seen since 1915 when I had had to clean them. He was a general, or perhaps a brigadier, grave and stout as becomes that high contemplative rank, but with a dry sense of humour, a quizzical expression, and eyes that sometimes twinkled. Evidently he had been advised of our coming, for without much questioning he dismissed us to our new place of confinement in a back alley off the bazaar.

The General's own house was one side of the alley, his kitchen and servants' quarters in a compound on the other. The cook and his assistant were cleared out to sleep on a veranda while we were put in their room. This was only a little larger than the Ishkashim cell and no less sparsely furnished. Here we had to stay under the eyes of a sentry—unarmed I was thankful to see—but we were allowed to walk in the compound or to sit on a bench by the kitchen door. There were no sanitary arrangements, so that we had to go out into the highways and by-ways attended always by the sentry. Apart from that we had few complaints. Our meals, which were probably the same as his, came direct from the General's kitchen, and I was delighted to find that he appreciated good food as much as the Commissar and took a lively interest in what went on in his kitchen. Very early in the morning one would find him, unshaven and wrapped in a 'chapkan', nosing around seeing what was toward. His eldest son was sick and had been seconded for duty as messing officer to the General's family, a nearby officers' mess, and now to ourselves. He was a model messing officer. He was always present to see our meals dished out, to wish us 'buon appetito', and to receive our praise. If we wanted anything from the bazaar, he would have it brought for us. He was only the second man I had come across in Afghanistan who could speak Hindustani fluently, so that in the nine dismal days we spent here we became good friends. All that we bought from the bazaar were some shoes for Yusuf's nag, some local soap and tobacco, which for all the good they were might well have been interchangeable, and a flannel shirt for myself which cost fifty Afghanis. My original shirt was not only in rags but was also fit food for the incinerator. In eating and scratching, we are told, everything is in the beginning. I had begun scratching at Ishkashim, I was still scratching at Faizabad—and with good reason. Even my new shirt went over to the enemy and that, too, had to be burnt at Chitral.

The programme proved to be much as I had feared. We must await the receipt of a telegram from Kabul which, according to the General, would take three or four days. We therefore settled down to wait with what hope or patience we could muster. Yusuf, now sunk again in profoundest gloom, retired under his 'poshteen', coming to the surface occasionally to ask me how far I thought it was to Kashmir. He now had the idea that we should do better to go to Kabul by bus, and when I pointed out that horses were not allowed on buses, airily suggested that the nag should be consigned to the care of some reliable Afghan to take to Srinagar by road. For my part I borrowed a pack of cards (only two were missing) from the cook's mate and played Patience grimly and unceasingly.

The only other diversion was watching what went on in the kitchen. The making of bread I found particularly fascinating. Every day the cook's mate had to turn out a couple of dozen loaves, or rather flat oval pieces nearly two feet long. Having made the dough and left it to rise he fired the oven. This had been built beneath the floor. It was about three feet deep and shaped like the inside of a jug, with the mouth a good deal narrower than the base. When the bottom of the oven was a glowing inferno of ashes the baker, having first wet his hand and forearm to prevent singeing, thrust his arm deep inside to plaster a piece of the slack dough on to the concave sloping side, running his hand up its length as he withdrew it. The bread acquired its long shape on the way in and it was this last stroking action which left the four characteristic deep furrows in the finished bread. Very rarely a piece failed to stick and became a total loss, the others swelled up, were baked, and peeled off in a matter of minutes.

We had arrived on the Monday and by Friday we learnt that not only had no telegram arrived but also that the Mahomedan festival of 'Id' began that day and that all business, including the dispatch of telegrams, would be suspended for four days. Everyone took a holiday except the cooks whose work redoubled, for the General was giving a lunch to all the Faizabad notabilities. He himself was early on the scene of action and having first submitted himself to the barber he spent an anxious morning in the kitchen, dealing out advice, encouragement, and occasionally abuse, and dispatching a stream of runners armed with a few copper coins to buy pennyworths of chillies, carrots, milk, tomatoes, or to hire mincing machines and crockery. When all was ready the General himself dished up, and before going to his guests brought Yusuf and me some of the choicer dishes with his own hands. A rich pilau was, of course, the solid core of a meal embellished with half a dozen spiced vegetable dishes and followed by a pudding, 'fit', as Heine said, 'for a glass case'.

The following day was the big day. It started off with gunfire from the fort, followed later by a second salvo which was the signal to assemble for prayer. Meanwhile, a couple of sheep had been slaughtered in aid of the General's staff and coloured hard-boiled eggs, sweets, and fruit were distributed to all and sundry, including the poor captives. Yusuf, on my strong recommendation, obtained permission to attend prayers. The Imam must have been a more powerful spell-binder than the Prophet of Baharak, for Yusuf appeared to have undergone a religious revival; from then on he prayed punctiliously five times a day, obtaining thereby solace and a fair amount of occupation; for at times he seemed to forget that he was on his knees and would spend whole minutes gazing reproachfully at me, the source of all his woes, or at the blank wall. I found his devout frame of mind (in which I could not partake) and his reproachful stare so disconcerting that in my games of Patience I very frequently overlooked the moving of a vital card.

On the Sunday a Sabbath calm reigned, although the fires of hospitality were still smouldering. Hosts of well-wishers came to salute the General and had to sit down to tea, fruit, and sweets. One began to feel sorry for the General lest his entertainment allowance should prove inadequate. Since, however, nothing stronger than tea was drunk it seemed likely that no great harm could come either to his pocket or to his guests. On Monday the smouldering fires blazed up once more. This time tables and chairs were set on the veranda adjoining our room, the battery of brass samovars in the compound was stoked up, and the whole day devoted to a desperate orgy of tea-drinking. The flow of visitors slackened not at all until towards evening, when the General and a few of the more obstinate guests settled down to chess. I was invited to play and it was not through any tact on my part that the General demolished me in a comparatively short time.

At supper that evening his son came in to ask how many ponies we needed for our journey to Chitral. Great was our relief and joy. I shook him rather unnecessarily by the hand while Yusuf once more spread his prayer carpet. A telegram ordering our release had come, but unfortunately there was a catch in it. I learnt next morning at the General's office that all my papers, less the passport, were to be sent to the Foreign Office at Kabul. Several hours were spent in an effort to save my diaries, but in the end, after taking a receipt, I was obliged to go without them. Before leaving I changed some more money with the General's son, during which I learnt that an Indian rupee was worth five Afghanis. The shifty Scholar had therefore received the equivalent of 500 Afghanis for twenty and a 'chapkan' worth eighty. The General's son indignantly denied Ghulam's claim to officer's rank, but whether it was a fact or whether he did it merely for the sake of the honour of Afghan officers I do not know. The General smiled at this successful deal in foreign exchange, but reached for the telephone and asked for a trunk call to Ishkashim—perhaps Ghulam eventually learnt something to his disadvantage.

And so we began to retrace our weary steps—not quite as far as Ish-kashim but to Zebak within a day's march of it. Now we were attended only by a solitary young soldier armed with a stick. This was reassuring to us, but it had its inconveniences in that a stick was less efficacious than a rifle for persuading villagers to provide food and transport. What they thought when they saw us returning—except that we were a damned nuisance—I cannot tell. Perhaps they accounted me a sort of Flying Dutchman doomed to ply backwards and forwards through Wakhan to the end of time, like a doomed soul rejected by heaven and hell and not really wanted on earth.

Of all the exasperating marches I have ever experienced this was the worst. Transport was hard to come by and harder still to keep, for our young soldier was no match either for bearded headmen or for the impudent beardless donkey-boys. We reached Baharak only by march-ing half the night, but the worst march was that through the last part of the Warduj gorge to the junction of the Ishkashim road and the valley leading south to Chitral. For this long stage we had but two unwilling donkeys driven by two still more unwilling urchins, with whom we had distressing and undignified scenes at each village in our efforts to force them onwards to the next. At the little village near the mouth of the gorge, fortune smiled on us and we found in the headman (a Pathan, I think) a man and brother, who gave us food without our asking, fresh donkeys, and a little 'lean, old, chapped, bald, shot of a man' who, when it came to driving them, was a human dynamo.

On the morning of the fifth day we reached Zebak at the foot of the Sanglich valley, a prosperous looking village surrounded by apricot orchards and walnut trees still bearing their foliage of brown, copper, and gold. It is bigger than Ishkashim and has a Commissar, too, who detained us for two hours while we answered his stupid questions. In spite of the soldier with us he was not satisfied, and rang up Faizabad before allowing us to proceed.

The telegraph line ends here, so now lest someone at Kabul took it into his head to stop us I decided to get as far as I could as quickly as possible. By three o'clock we had reached Isitich, ten miles short of Sanglich village. The usual crowd gathered round us; but this time without waiting for the soldier to utter a half-hearted apologetic request for a fresh baggage pony I pulled out a twenty-Afghani note.

That did the trick. I handed over an earnest of ten and within five minutes we had changed loads and were off again. At Sanglich, which we reached at dark, we found an Afghan post in charge of an officer to whom our soldier handed a note from the General. It was a potent talisman, for this handsome, swashbuckling captain in well-cut greatcoat and peaked cap was at once all over us, paying us polite attentions until late at night, and then coming back early in the morning with breakfast and a promise of transport.

This promise was not so easily fulfilled. It seemed that the good people of Sanglich, aware of what might be expected of them, had taken steps to have their animals either out of the way or in use. Unluckily for the owner, the nag which I had hired yesterday foolishly stuck its head out of a stable. The captain saw it and before the poor beast knew what was happening it was being loaded by half a dozen soldiers. The owner put up a spirited resistance—the horse was lame, he was sick, his wife was dying—but his clamour went unheeded. Across the Dorah pass he must go with his horse or suffer penalties. The captain posed for a photograph, begged me earnestly to say nothing of any part of my stay in his country which had not been to my liking, shook me warmly by the hand and wished me good luck.

The young soldier now returned and his place was taken by a very short blackguard, whose duty it was to accompany me to Chitral in order to obtain an official receipt for the body. That he had the misfortune to be dressed as an Afghan soldier was possibly not his fault, but it damned him in my eyes. Still he had his points. Instead of bawling at me when he wanted me to stop, turn, or go on, he whistled gently like a poacher to his dog. He could walk as the others could not, and since he wanted to get back he walked fast. The Dorah pass, just under 15,000 ft., is the easiest pass over the Hindu Kush between Badakshan and Chitral, and is about fifty-five miles from Chitral town itself. The route is much used by Afghan traders and horse-dealers.

When we left Sanglich it was a fine morning but so cold that the water furrows were all frozen. Seven miles farther on the valley forks and we turned up the left-hand branch where half a mile up we came to the last Afghan outpost, an indescribably dirty hovel in which three unkempt Afghan soldiers blended harmoniously with the squalor as they dozed away their time. To me such a post was now a familiar sight and one upon which I looked for the last time without a shadow of regret. By midday we were near the foot of the pass with a great deal of steep climbing in front of us. The path follows the shore of a mile-long lake of deepest blue, the Hauz-i-Dorah or Lake Dufferin, which is surrounded on three sides by some impressively glaciated though not very high mountains. We turned away on to steep grass and rubble slopes up which we laboured for the next three hours. Either because of the forced marches of the last few days or because of a cough I had now acquired I found it trying. Yusuf and the 'short blackguard' seemed much less distressed than I was, but could go no faster, as their pace was governed by the horses they were leading. Snow began falling as we crossed the wide drift-strewn plain just below the summit.

I made for the cairn and gazed down unbelievingly into Chitral. Were we really free or was there some other surprise in wait? The one side appeared as bleak, inhospitable, and uncharitable, as I knew the other to be—a tangle of trivial peaks, rock ridges, and deep scored valleys. My satisfaction was immense, shorn though the scene was of all the adjuncts I had wished for. There was no Afghan boundary stone marked out for ceremonial desecration, no diaries (alas!) to be laid at my feet, and if the 'short blackguard' felt any inclination to salute, he managed to suppress it.

Yusuf, though disappointed to find no tangible evidence that we were on the threshold of the great British raj, gaily mounted his nag, now ribby, wayworn, and lean, and begged me to take his photograph. For the last two days he had been visibly perking up, and his religious zeal, I was sorry to note, had diminished. If his religion was a sheet anchor to be used only in storm, he was casting it off much too soon. Had he but known it he was not nearly out of the wood and his cup of sorrow not nearly full. The war in Kashmir, which we first heard of next day, prevented his going there, where, in fact, he had never any reason to go, for he was presently to learn from a Turkoman trader in Chitral that his poor old father was not in Kashmir at all, but Lhasa. Finally, though we had just passed a month with the wicked without suffering the loss of a hair, the very first night at Chitral they stripped the clothes—a valuable saddle-cloth—from the back of his nag. Thus, his mission unaccomplished and his filial duty unfulfilled, he had to return alone by a weary and devious way through Gilgit back to Kashgar, getting himself nearly drowned in a river (as I heard later) on the way.

But these bleak prospects were fortunately hidden and there on the Dorah pass I think he forgave me. As I, I suppose, must forgive the Afghans, particularly those who stand most in need of forgiveness, the Commissar, the Shifty Scholar, and the entire garrison of Ishkashim; but to the General, whose attentions shone like a good deed in a naughty world, I give not forgiveness but grateful thanks. For if one lives in a buffer state one must, I suppose, act like a buffer and repel everything, from individuals to army corps. And who are the Afghans that they should have heard of a brave new world of visa-less travel to which I, one of the early exponents, had fallen a sacrifice? Still, since the Afghans and the British have been neighbours now for a good many years, even fighting occasionally as these will, their behaviour on the whole was, I thought, unneighbourly; for, as the Chinese proverb says, 'when a neighbour is in your garden inattention is the truest politeness.'

For me it had been a season conspicuously lacking in success. Every enterprise had either failed or led me into trouble. But man is born to trouble, and failure is such a common occurrence in men's affairs that most of us have at our fingers' ends some trite but nevertheless true sayings calculated to lessen the sting of defeat and to turn adversity to our advantage. Seneca, I think, has asserted that to escape misfortune is to want instruction, and that to live in ease is to live in ignorance; and as I turned to go down into Chitral, tired, lousy, and bereft of my diaries, I felt that the year had at any rate been rich in instruction.

H. W. TILMAN

The Collected Edition

FOR THE FIRST TIME SINCE THEIR ORIGINAL APPEARANCE, all fifteen books by H. W. Tilman are being published as single volumes, with all their original photographs, maps and charts. Forewords and afterwords by those who knew him, or who can bring their own experience and knowledge to bear, complement his own understated writing to give us a fuller picture of the man and his achievements. A sixteenth volume is the 1980 biography by J. R. L. Anderson, *High Mountains and Cold Seas*. The books will appear in pairs, one each from his climbing and sailing eras, in order of original publication, at quarterly intervals from September 2015:

www.tilmanbooks.com